Study Guide for

Man, Nature, and Society

Study Guide for
Man, Nature, and Society
an introduction to biology

Theodore W. Pohrte
Dallas County Community College District

L. Jack Pierce
Mountain View College

Wm. C. Brown Company Publishers
Dubuque, Iowa

wcb

Printed in the United States of America

Contents

Introduction

YOUR STUDY GUIDE

Purpose. This *Study Guide* is designed to aid you in your study of Dr. E. Peter Volpe's *Man, Nature, and Society*. The guide is organized and sequenced in a way found to be helpful to students, particularly those in the early stages of their college experience. We encourage you to read the entire introduction carefully and follow the recommended learning activities completely and conscientiously. If you do, you should find you are using your study time more effectively, and your level of achievement should be correspondingly higher.

Contents. Your *Study Guide* contains one complete module for each chapter of *Man, Nature, and Society*. With a few exceptions, all modules have the same elements. These elements—their purpose and use—are described below.

MODULE ELEMENTS

Overview. Each module begins with an overview, which introduces the central ideas of the chapter, sets the stage for the principal learning goals, and indicates the philosophical thrust of the module. You might use it to help organize your thoughts and attitudes as you begin your study of the chapter. The overview is most useful if read *before* you read the corresponding chapter.

Learning Goals. To help you focus your study, the main ideas in the chapter are expressed as learning goals. By fully achieving these goals, you should be able to do well on the posttest and on examinations designed to match these goals. To be of most help, the learning goals should be read *before* you read the chapter; then keep them in mind as you complete your study.

Pretest. You may already know some of the central ideas in the chapter from previous experience. The pretest should:

1. alert you to the main concepts to be learned;
2. tell you what you already know about these concepts—and more importantly, what you do not know;
3. give you an indication of how much you learned when you compare your pretest score with your score on the posttest.

The pretest should be most helpful if you complete it *before* you read the chapter. The pretests and posttests are designed to be *self* tests. The pretest questions are also designed to be used as *study questions.*

Vocabulary. A major key to learning new concepts is the acquisition of a working knowledge of the words—mostly technical terms and phrases—used to express the concepts. As a general learning goal, implicit in each module, you should write the definitions of all of the listed words and practice using them, *orally* and *in writing,* until they become part of your working vocabulary.

Study Exercises. Study exercises are provided for additional practice on principal ideas in each chapter. The more carefully and completely you write your answers to these exercises, as well as the study (pretest) questions, the better you should perform on examinations.

Probe. Many of the modules contain an additional element: *probe.* The probe section asks one or more questions of an attitudinal, or personal opinion, nature. These questions provide an opportunity for you to analyze and synthesize facts, concepts, and attitudes, then reach a conclusion based upon your judgment—and your viewpoint.

Posttest. The posttest provides a check of your achievement of the learning goals. By answering each of the questions without referring to other materials, as might be expected on a proctored (class) examination, you can identify concepts you need to review again. By comparing your pretest and posttest scores, you will have an indication of how much you learned in that chapter. Your corrected responses to the test questions should be very useful as you review for examinations.

Answers. The last element in each module of the *Study Guide* is that of answers to the pretest. Providing answers to the test questions greatly enhances their usefulness for self-evaluation. You will be able to check your answers and review questions that you missed as soon as you have completed the test, while the questions are still fresh in your mind.

Chapter 1

Seeds of Life

OVERVIEW

It is important that each of us have an accurate concept of mammalian reproductive activities, if for no other reason than to know how we were produced. The reproductive system must be observed and studied as any other body system, not tossed aside as a mystery. Materials are presented in this chapter that will allow you to mentally construct a model of the physiological and anatomical processes of mammalian reproduction.

LEARNING GOALS

After successfully completing this chapter you should be able to do the following, orally or in writing.

1. Relate early biological investigations to present concepts.
2. List several early theories concerning the development of the animal embryo.
3. Develop an understanding of the vocabulary associated with reproduction and embryonic development.
4. Compare the ova (egg) types and numbers of selected vertebrate animals.
5. State the role of hormones in regulating the menstrual cycle.
6. Explain the association between the hypothalamus and pituitary (hypophysis).
7. Describe the structure of the mammalian male and female reproductive systems.
8. Discuss the process of ejaculation, ovulation, and fertilization with respect to the mammal.
9. Describe the process of estrus in mammals as related to sexual activity.
10. Describe what the terms *chromosome, gene, DNA, gamete,* and *zygote* mean.
11. Relate how the genetic code regulates the ultimate outcome of an individual from fertilization through birth and ending with death.

SELF-PRETEST OF LEARNING GOALS

Before proceeding further in the study of this chapter, attempt to answer the following questions without referring to other information. Upon completion of the test, compare your responses with the answer key at the end of the *Study Guide* chapter. Then correct the wrong responses by referring to the text (page numbers are indicated following each question).

Matching

1. Harvey (p. 3)
2. de Graaf (p. 5)
3. Falloppio (p. 6)
4. Fraenkel (p. 10)
5. Bonnet (p. 3)

a. human blood circulation
b. coined the term *ovaries*
c. observed oviducts connected to uterus
d. ovary is functional other than egg production
e. theory of emboîtement

Multiple Choice

6. Which type of animal releases jelly-protected eggs into the water? (p. 4)
   a. Amphibian
   b. Reptile
   c. Bird
   d. Mammal
   e. None of these

7. Which type of animal releases the largest number of eggs? (p. 5)
   a. Amphibian
   b. Fish
   c. Bird
   d. Mammal
   e. Reptile

8. Approximately how often does the human female ovary have a follicle rupture? (p. 6)
   a. Every 20 days
   b. Every 28 days
   c. Every 14 days
   d. Every 7 days
   e. None of these

9. The oviduct is also known as the (p. 6)
   a. vagina.
   b. Fallopian tube.
   c. Graafian follicle.
   d. uterus.
   e. clitoris.

10. Where, normally, in the mammalian female does the process of fertilization occur? (p. 7)
    a. Vagina
    b. Uterus
    c. Ovary
    d. Fallopian tube
    e. None of these
    f. Clitoris

11. Approximately how long after ovulation does the human egg remain fertile? (p. 7)
    a. 5 hours
    b. 8 hours
    c. 3 days
    d. 1 week
    e. None of these
    f. 1 day

Fill in the Blank

12. The internal (inner) wall of the uterus is known as the _____. (p. 7)

13. Another term for the uterus is the _____. (p. 7)

14. The erectile tissue of the female that corresponds to the male penis is known as the _____. (p. 8)

15. The uterus terminates in the _____, which projects into the upper part of the vagina. (p. 7)

16. The tube that leads from the bladder to the exterior is the _____. (p. 8)

17. Menopause normally occurs in the human female at approximately _____ years of age. (p. 9)

18. The name of the glandlike structure that is formed from the follicle is known as the _____. (p. 10)

True—False

19. FSH is produced (synthesized) by the pituitary (hypophysis). (p. 11)
    a. True
    b. False

20. The growing follicle produces a hormone of its own called *estrogen.* (p. 12)
    a. True   b. False

21. Ovulation normally occurs in the human female around day 14 of the menstrual cycle. (p. 12)
    a. True   b. False

22. The essential hormones of "the pill" are estrogen and progesteron. (p. 13)
    a. True   b. False

23. The hypothalamus, a part of the brain, actually controls the pituitary. (p. 13)
    a. True   b. False

24. Estrus in the human female occurs every 28 days. (p. 14)
    a. True   b. False

Matching (Answers may be used more than once.)

25. Scrotum (p. 15)   a. found in female only
26. Acrosome (p. 15)   b. found in male only
27. Labia majora (p. 8)   c. found in both sexes
28. Urethra (pp. 8, 17)
29. Corpus albicans (p. 10)
30. Vas deferens (p. 17)
31. FSH (pp. 11, 16)
32. Corpa cavernosa (p. 17)
33. Hyaluronidase (p. 18)
34. Chromosomes (p. 19)

Fill in the Blank

35. The complex molecule known as ＿＿＿＿＿＿ (p. 19) comprises the gene.

36. The interstitial cells produce the hormone ＿＿＿＿＿＿. (pp. 15, 16)

37. The term applied to the sperm and the fluid from the accessory glands is ＿＿＿＿＿＿. (p. 17)

38. Man contains ＿＿＿＿＿＿ chromosomes in every body cell. (p. 19)

VOCABULARY

These are key words that you should know. By learning these words you will achieve learning goal number 3. The text page on which the respective definition occurs is indicated following the word.

 1. vertebrate (p. 4)   13. labia minora (p. 8)
 2. yolk (p. 4)   14. clitoris (p. 8)
 3. zona pellucida (p. 5)   15. labia majora (p. 8)
 4. corona radiata (p. 5)   16. urethra (p. 8)
 5. follicle (p. 6)   17. ovary (pp. 5, 9)
 6. ovulation (p. 6)   18. atresia (p. 10)
 7. Fallopian tube (p. 6)   19. corpus luteum (p. 10)
 8. uterus (p. 7)   20. corpus albicans (p. 10)
 9. endometrium (p. 7)   21. pituitary gland (p. 11)
10. menstruation (p. 7)   22. gonadotrophic hormones (p. 11)
11. cervix (p. 7)   23. estrogen (p. 12)
12. vagina (p. 8)   24. progesterone (p. 12)

25. proliferative and secretory phase (p. 12)
26. contraceptives (p. 13)
27. hypothalamus (p. 13)
28. estrus (p. 14)
29. pseudopregnancy (p. 14)
30. sperm and hyaluronidase (pp. 15, 18)
31. testes and seminiferous tubules (p. 15)
32. testosterone (p. 16)

33. ICSH (p. 16)
34. epididymis (p. 17)
35. vas deferens and vasectomy (p. 17)
36. seminal vesicles and prostate (p. 17)
37. semen (p. 17)
38. penis (p. 17)
39. chromosomes, genes, DNA (p. 19)
40. genetic code (p. 19)

STUDY EXERCISES

Instructions: Write out your answers carefully and completely on separate paper. Check your answers by referring to the text page indicated.

1. How do the eggs of vertebrates compare and differ? (pp. 4, 5, 14)
2. Briefly describe the process of ovulation and the role of the corpus luteum in the mammalian female. (pp. 6-15)
3. Describe anatomically the mammalian male and female reproductive systems. (pp. 5-17)
4. How is the human menstrual cycle controlled by hormones? (pp. 11-13)
5. What role does the hypothalamus have? (p. 13)
6. What are chromosomes? What is their relation to genes? What is their relation to DNA? (p. 19)

SELF-POSTTEST OF LEARNING GOALS

Instructions: After completing the vocabulary in written form it is now time to review. State each definition orally several times. Reread those areas in your text associated with the study exercises on which you did poorly. Retake the pretest at this time.

ANSWERS

1. a
2. b
3. c
4. d
5. e
6. a
7. b
8. b
9. b
10. d
11. e
12. endometrium
13. womb
14. clitoris
15. cervix
16. urethra
17. 45-50
18. corpus luteum
19. a

20. a
21. a
22. a
23. a
24. b
25. b
26. b
27. a
28. c
29. a
30. b
31. c
32. b
33. b
34. c
35. DNA
36. testosterone
37. semen
38. 46

Chapter 2

Control of Fertility

OVERVIEW

The increasing numbers of persons on this planet is causing everyone to look long and hard at methods for controlling population. It is necessary that you realize that the ever-increasing population is placing an extreme strain on the planet Earth through consumption of natural resources and pollution. It is apparent that if we are to survive on this planet the numbers of births must be drastically reduced. In this chapter various types of birth control methods will be discussed with emphasis placed on the reliability of each method.

LEARNING GOALS

After successfully completing this chapter you should be able to do the following, orally or in writing.

1. Describe the historical aspects of birth control by relating the chronology of the control of fertility, terminating with the advent of "the pill."
2. Describe coitus interruptus and state the reason for the high failure rate of this control method.
3. Discuss why there is a universal acceptance of the condom and what the initial reason for its development was.
4. Relate why douching is limited in its effectiveness.
5. Describe the effectiveness of various types of chemical spermicides and mechanical barriers.
6. Analyze the rhythm method from both a procedural and biological standpoint.
7. State the physiological basis by which the oral contraceptive operates.
8. Relate the favorable and unfavorable attributes of "the pill" based on the infinite number of articles that regularly appear in popular magazines.
9. Describe the development of the IUD, discuss the various types presently in use, and analyze the theories of the mode of action of the IUD.
10. Analyze the procedures of sterilization and project your own concepts of the validity of sterilization.
11. Describe the procedures of a hospital abortion.
12. State the basis for the Catholic doctrine prohibiting birth control.
13. Speculate on future controls that may be used to stabilize fertility.
14. Define the various terms or phrases new to you concerning birth control.

SELF-PRETEST OF LEARNING GOALS

Before proceeding further in the study of this chapter, attempt to answer the following questions without referring to other information. Upon completion of the test, compare your responses with the answer key at the end of the *Study Guide* chapter. Then correct the wrong responses by referring to the text (page numbers are indicated following each question).

Multiple Choice

1. Contraceptive techniques and devices have been used for approximately_____
   years. (p. 23)
   - a. 100
   - b. 1,000
   - c. None of these
   - d. 3,500
   - e. 500

2. Which of the following was the first modern device used for birth control? (p. 23)
   - a. IUD
   - b. Condom
   - c. Pill
   - d. Foam
   - e. Diaphragm

3. Coitus interruptus is associated with which of the following? (p. 24)
   - a. None of these
   - b. IUD
   - c. Withdrawal
   - d. Condom
   - e. Foam

4. Which of the following would be classed as a mechanical barrier? (pp. 24-26)
   - a. Diaphragm
   - b. Condom
   - c. Cervical cap
   - d. None of these
   - e. All of these

5. Which of the following represents an acceptable birth control method as established by the Roman Catholic Church? (p. 27)
   - a. IUD
   - b. Condom
   - c. Pill
   - d. Rhythm method
   - e. None of these

6. Which of the following represents the hormone combination observed in the oral contraceptive ("the pill")? (p. 31)
   - a. Adrenalin and estrogen
   - b. Mestranol and estrogen
   - c. Progesterone and adrenalin
   - d. Estrogen and progesterone
   - e. Progesterone and norene
   - f. None of these

7. When was "the pill" introduced to American women? (p. 24)
   - a. None of these
   - b. 1890
   - c. Mid-1920s
   - d. 1951
   - e. Early 1960s
   - f. Late 1940s

8. Other than "the pill," which contraceptive method has the lowest failure rate? (p. 34)
   - a. Condom
   - b. IUD
   - c. Diaphragm
   - d. Rhythm method
   - e. Vaginal foam
   - f. None of these

True—False

9. The first oral contraceptive allowed for public use in the early 1960s was *Enovid.* (p. 24)
   - a. True
   - b. False

10. The control of fertility failure rate is low in coitus interruptus. (p. 24)
    - a. True
    - b. False

11. The first drops of semen expelled usually contain high concentrations of sperm. (p. 24)
    - a. True
    - b. False

12. The most widely used contraceptive device is the condom. (p. 24)
   a. True   b. False

13. Chemical preparations such as creams, jellies, or foams act by immobilizing the egg. (p. 26)
   a. True   b. False

14. The diaphragm must remain in place for at least 24 hours after intercourse. (p. 27)
   a. True   b. False

15. The high rate of failure of the rhythm method is largely due to irregularities of the menstrual cycles of women. (p. 27)
   a. True   b. False

16. There are at least 20 different kinds of "the pill," but all fall essentially into two general categories: the combined type and the sequential type. (p. 31)
   a. True   b. False

17. "The pill" alters the normal activity of the pituitary. (pp. 31, 32)
   a. True   b. False

18. The shape of the IUD apparently affects efficiency, with the spiral and the loop being the most effective. (pp. 34, 35)
   a. True   b. False

19. Since the Supreme Court ruling of 1973, abortion by mechanical means is legal in the United States. (p. 36)
   a. True   b. False

20. At present there are no satisfactory methods for controlling fertility in the male. (p. 39)
   a. True   b. False

Matching

21. Falloppio (p. 23)
22. Sanger (p. 23)
23. Rock (p. 24)
24. Gräfenberg (p. 23)
25. Pincus (p. 23)

a. founded American birth control movement in 1913
b. early progesterone research, 1951
c. none of these
d. gynecologist associated with clinical tests in 1956
e. developed the first condom in 1564
f. popularized IUD in 1920s

VOCABULARY

These are key words that you should know. By learning these words you will achieve learning goal number 15. The page where the respective definition occurs is indicated following the word.

1. contraception (p. 24)
2. condom (pp. 23-25)
3. Enovid (p. 24)
4. coitus interruptus (p. 24)
5. douche (p. 26)
6. spermicides (p. 26)
7. diaphragm (pp. 26, 27)
8. rhythm method (pp. 27-30)

9. oral contraceptive (p. 31)
10. mestranol (p. 31)
11. norethynodrel (p. 31)
12. pill (combined) (pp. 31-33)
13. pill (sequential) (pp. 31, 32)
14. LH and FSH (p. 32)
15. estrogen (p. 31)
16. progesterone (pp. 31, 33)

17. pituitary gland (p. 31)
18. thromboembolism (p. 33)
19. IUD (pp. 33, 34)
20. vasectomy (pp. 35, 36)
21. tubal ligation (p. 36)
22. abortion (pp. 36-38)

23. curette (p. 37)
24. D and C (p. 37)
25. vacuum aspiration (p. 37)
26. postcoital pill (p. 38)
27. prostaglandins (pp. 38, 39)

STUDY EXERCISES

Instructions: Write out your answers carefully and completely on a separate paper. Check your answers by referring to the text page indicated.

1. Briefly describe some of the historical aspects of fertility control. (pp. 23, 24)
2. Describe your personal feelings concerning the various types of contraceptive methods (condom, diaphragm, IUD, etc.). Relate whether you would use them and, if not, describe specifically why not.
3. How does the diaphragm prevent pregnancy? (pp. 26, 27)
4. Basically, what is the principle of the rhythm method? (pp. 27-30)
5. Describe, physiologically, the action of the oral contraceptive ("the pill"). (pp. 31, 32)
6. Briefly describe the subsequent effect of a vasectomy and tubal ligation on the male and female respectively. (pp. 35, 36)

OTHER ACTIVITIES

1. Interview close friends (peers) as well as older persons and pose questions that would relate to philosophies about contraception. Record answers to specific questions that you have previously formulated.
2. Read popular articles concerning attitudes of society and religions toward fertility control. Attempt to broaden your knowledge of fertility control by becoming involved in various experiences as related above.

PROBE

1. Compare the current philosophies of abortion as they relate to society, religion, and your own concepts.
2. Do you think governments should have the right to force birth control? In your answer consider a government that is forced to such a decision because of overpopulation or lack of food.
3. At what age do you think an individual should be educated about birth control? At what age should contraceptive devices be made available?
4. When do you think life begins? Is it at fertilization, implantation, three months, etc.? How do you arrive at your answer? (pp. 37, 38 provide background)

SELF-POSTTEST OF LEARNING GOALS

Instructions: After completing the vocabulary in written form it is now time to review. State each definition orally several times. Reread those areas in your text associated with the study exercises on which you did poorly. Retake the pretest at this time.

ANSWERS

1. d	14. b
2. b	15. a
3. c	16. a
4. e	17. a
5. d	18. a
6. d	19. a
7. e	20. a
8. b	21. e
9. a	22. a
10. b	23. d
11. a	24. f
12. a	25. b
13. b	

Chapter 3

Development, Implantation, and Placentation

OVERVIEW

In this chapter the process of embryonic development is discussed. Emphasis is placed on the chronological order of tissue and system differentiation and growth. Current research in artificial implantation is presented.

LEARNING GOALS

After successfully completing this chapter you should be able to do the following, orally or in writing.

1. Describe the process of cleavage.
2. Discuss the formation and role of the extraembryonic membranes of various vertebrates.
3. Relate the types of germ cells to the tissues that result from their differentiation.
4. Analyze the role of the mammalian placenta.
5. Describe the specific hormonal changes during pregnancy.
6. Discuss the embryonic changes that are the result of tissue differentiation.
7. Formulate arguments for and against the possible future control of human development (for example, test tube babies and artificial insemination).
8. Define the various terms or phrases new to you concerning the process of embryonic development.

SELF-PRETEST OF LEARNING GOALS

Before proceeding further in the study of this chapter, attempt to answer the following questions without referring to other information. Upon completion of the test, compare your responses with the answer key at the end of the *Study Guide* chapter. Then correct the wrong responses by referring to the text (page numbers are indicated following each question).

Fill in the Blank

1. The successive divisions of the egg are referred to as _____ . (p. 43)

2. It takes the fertilized human egg approximately_____ days to implant in the uterus. (p. 43)

3. At the time of implantation the embryo resembles a hollow sphere known as the _____.
   (p. 43)

4. The tissue system that is the barrier between the mother and fetus is known as the _____.
   (pp. 44, 45)

5. The mammalian mother disposes of fetal wastes through her _____ and_____.
   (p. 45)

6. The extraembryonic membranes are the _____ , _____ , and_____.
   (p. 46)

True—False

7. After approximately 120 days of fetal development the mixing of the mother's blood and that of the fetus occurs. (p. 45)
   a. True
   b. False

8. The human embryo develops a yolk sac. (p. 49)
   a. True
   b. False

9. The chorion is the most highly specialized extraembryonic membrane. (p. 49)
   a. True
   b. False

10. The umbilical cord contains two veins and an artery. (p. 51)
    a. True
    b. False

11. The umbilical blood vessels are the counterpart of the allantoic blood vessels found in the developing egg of the chicken. (p. 51)
    a. True
    b. False

Multiple Choice

12. Which of the following release progesterone? (p. 52)
    a. Pituitary
    b. Embryo
    c. Uterus
    d. Corpus luteum
    e. Corpus albicans
    f. None of these

13. Which of the following secrete chorionic gonadotrophin? (p. 52)
    a. Pituitary
    b. Embryo
    c. Uterus
    d. Corpus luteum
    e. Corpus albicans
    f. None of these

14. Which of the following secrete estrogen and progesterone? (p. 53)
    a. Ovary
    b. Embryo
    c. Placenta
    d. Pituitary
    e. Two of these
    f. Three of these
    g. All of these
    h. None of these

Matching

Order of embryonic appearance. Place the answers listed in the order in which each occurs.

15. First _____
16. Second _____
17. Third _____
18. Fourth _____
19. Fifth _____
20. Sixth _____
21. Seventh _____

a. mesoderm (p. 48)

b. allantois (p. 47)

c. chorion (pp. 49, 50)

d. placenta (p. 50)

e. morula (p. 43)

f. eyes formed (p. 55)

g. trophoblast (pp. 49, 50)

True—False

22. The unborn child is almost completely formed by the time it completes its eighth week of development. (p. 56)
    a. True   b. False

23. If a sperm and egg unite in a test tube the process is said to have occurred *in vitro*. (p. 56)
    a. True   b. False

24. Human embryos contain gill arches early in development. (p. 54)
    a. True   b. False

25. By the end of the fifth week the sex of the human embryo is easily determined. (p. 55)
    a. True   b. False

26. The placenta produces progesterone. (p. 53)
    a. True   b. False

27. Progesterone is produced by the corpus luteum. (p. 52)
    a. True   b. False

VOCABULARY

These are key words that you should know. By learning these words you will achieve learning goal number 8. The page where the respective definition occurs is indicated following the word.

 1. cleavage (p. 43)
 2. morula (p. 43)
 3. implantation (p. 43)
 4. blastocoel (p. 43)
 5. blastocyst (p. 43)
 6. trophoblast (p. 43)
 7. maternal (p. 45)
 8. placenta (p. 44)
 9. yolk (p. 46)
10. amnion (p. 46)
11. chorion (p. 46)
12. allantois (pp. 46, 47)
13. yolk sac (p. 49)
14. amniotic fluid (p. 47)
15. ectoderm (pp. 48, 49)
16. mesoderm (pp. 48, 49)
17. endoderm (pp. 48, 49)
18. monotreme (p. 49)
19. villus (pp. 50, 51)
20. parturition (p. 51)
21. labor (p. 51)
22. afterbirth (p. 51)
23. corpus luteum (p. 52)
24. chorionic gonadotrophin (p. 52)
25. Ascheim-Zondek test (p. 53)
26. vertebrate (p. 55)
27. fetus (p. 55)
28. laparoscopy (p. 56)

STUDY EXERCISES

Instructions: Write out your answers carefully and completely on a separate paper. Check your answers by referring to the text page indicated.

1. Briefly discuss the process of cleavage. (p. 43)
2. Describe the formation of the trophoblast. (pp. 43, 44)
3. Compare the development of the extraembryonic membranes of the chick and the human. (pp. 46-51)
4. Briefly relate the development of the human placenta. (pp. 49-53)
5. Where are chorionic gonadotrophins produced? How do they cause a positive pregnancy test? (pp. 52, 53)

PROBE

1. What is your personal opinion concerning the artificial implantation of a female with an already developing embryo? What was the basis for your opinion? (pp. 56-58 for background)
2. Suppose a married couple had not been able to have children. Upon physical examination it was found that the husband could not produce sperm but the wife was normal. How would you react to a suggestion that the wife undergo artificial insemination using the sperm from an unknown healthy male donor?

SELF-POSTTEST OF LEARNING GOALS

Instructions: After completing the vocabulary in written form it is now time to review. State each definition orally several times. Reread those areas in your text associated with the study exercises on which you did poorly. Retake the pretest at this time.

ANSWERS

1. cleavage
2. seven
3. blastocyst
4. placenta
5. lungs and kidneys
6. amnion, chorion, and allantois
7. b
8. a
9. a
10. b
11. a
12. d
13. b
14. e
15. e
16. g
17. a
18. b
19. c
20. d
21. f
22. a
23. a
24. a
25. b
26. a
27. a

Chapter 4

Molecules of Life and Placental Transfer

OVERVIEW

All cells are in a state of continuous and intense chemical activity. This chapter emphasizes the transformation of nutrients (foods) into complex molecules or into energy. It is the ability of the cell to convert carbohydrates (primary conversion) and fats and proteins (secondary conversion) into molecules that can be oxidized, or "burned." This provides the energy that insures the livability of not only the cell, but tissues, organ systems, and the animal itself. This chapter primarily treats the nutritional requirements of the human fetus. However, you must understand that principles given are applicable to any animal or any cell.

LEARNING GOALS

After successfully completing this chapter you should be able to do the following, orally or in writing.

1. Define organic compound, carbohydrate, fat, and protein.
2. Compare the basic structures of monosaccharides, disaccharides, and polysaccharides.
3. Identify the plant and animal storage form of carbohydrates.
4. Identify the principal storage centers of glycogen in the animal.
5. Describe how a molecule of fat is formed.
6. Describe how a phospholipid is formed.
7. Relate the various physiological activities associated with proteins.
8. Describe how proteins are synthesized (made).
9. Discuss how food (nutrients) found in the mother's blood eventually reaches cells of the fetus.
10. Define semipermeability with respect to cell membranes.
11. Relate how simple diffusion and oxygen transfer occur between the maternal and fetal circulation.
12. Describe the various mechanisms that assure homeostasis.
13. Describe facilitated diffusion.
14. Briefly relate how high-molecular-weight proteins that are present in the mother's blood are made available to the fetus.
15. State several activities that may be undertaken by the mother that have been shown to interfere with the proper development of the fetus.
16. Explain how a fetus can develop in the uterus of the mother without being rejected as though it were a foreign tissue.
17. Use appropriately the vocabulary associated with this chapter when discussing the concepts presented.

SELF-PRETEST OF LEARNING GOALS

Before proceeding further in the study of this chapter, attempt to answer the following questions without referring to other information. Upon completion of the test, compare your responses with the answer key at the end of the *Study Guide* chapter. Then correct the wrong responses by referring to the text (page numbers are indicated following each question).

Multiple Choice (Answers may be used more than once or not at all.)

1. Organic compounds always contain which of the following elements? (p. 61)
   a. Carbon
   b. Nitrogen
   c. Phosphorus
   d. Potassium
   e. Oxygen
   f. None of these

2. Carbohydrates always contain which of the following elements? (p. 62)
   a. Carbon and oxygen
   b. Oxygen and nitrogen
   c. Carbon, oxygen, and nitrogen
   d. Carbon, oxygen, and phosphorus
   e. Oxygen, carbon, and hydrogen
   f. None of these

3. Which of the following is a monosaccharide? (p. 62)
   a. Starch
   b. Sucrose
   c. Glucose
   d. Glycogen
   e. None of these
   f. Glycine

4. What is the chemical formula of glucose? (p. 62)
   a. $C_6 H_{12} O_6$
   b. $C_{12} H_{22} O_{11}$
   c. $C_6 H_{10} O_5$
   d. None of these
   e. $C_{27} H_{55} O_{11}$
   f. $C_3 H_6 O_3$

5. Which of the following is a disaccharide? (p. 62)
   a. Glucose
   b. Fructose
   c. Galactose
   d. Sucrose
   e. Starch
   f. Glycogen

6. Which of the following are polysaccharides? (p. 62)
   a. Starch
   b. Glycine
   c. Glycogen
   d. Fructose
   e. Glucose
   f. Sucrose

7. In the human the principal storage areas for glycogen are the (p. 63)
   a. liver and kidney.
   b. muscle and spleen.
   c. liver and muscle.
   d. liver and spleen.
   e. lung and liver.
   f. liver and brain.

8. Another term for fat is (p. 63)
   a. sugar.
   b. carbohydrate.
   c. protein.
   d. lipid.
   e. phosphate.
   f. none of these.

9. Fats always contain which of the following elements? (p. 63)
   a. Carbon, hydrogen, and oxygen
   b. Carbon, oxygen, and nitrogen
   c. Nitrogen, carbon, and potassium
   d. Carbon, oxygen, and nitrogen
   e. Oxygen, carbon, and phosphorus
   f. None of these

10. A molecule of fat is formed by the union of (p. 63)
    a. fatty acids and glycerol.
    b. glycogen and sugar.
    c. alcohol and glycogen.
    d. protein and phosphorus.
    e. none of these.
    f. fatty acids and nitrogen.

11. Proteins always contain which of the following elements? (p. 64)
    (C=carbon; N=nitrogen; O=oxygen; Na=sodium; H=hydrogen; P=phosphorus; K=potassium)
    a. C,H,O,P
    b. C,H,O,Na
    c. C,H,O,N
    d. C,H,O,N,P,Na
    e. C,H,N,P
    f. C,H,O,N,K

12. Which of the following are proteins? (pp. 63, 64)
    a. Insulin
    b. Hemoglobin
    c. Myosin
    d. All of these
    e. None of these
    f. Lactoglobulin

13. The basic building blocks of proteins are (p. 64)
    a. sugars.
    b. amino acids.
    c. fats.
    d. lipids.
    e. all of these.
    f. none of these.

Fill in the Blank

14. All amino acids contain one amino chemical group and one _____ group. (p. 64)

15. The simplest amino acid is _____ . (p. 66)

16. A chain of several amino acids is referred to as a _____ . (p. 66)

17. There are _____ different amino acids. (pp. 64, 66)

18. The transfer of soluble nutritive substances from the mother's blood stream occurs through the walls of the chorionic _____ . (p. 67)

19. The breakdown of glucose to obtain energy in the absence of oxygen is known as _____ . (p. 70)

20. _____ are substances capable of causing marked developmental deviations. (p. 73)

True—False

21. Semipermeable membranes allow certain molecules to pass while blocking others. (p. 68)
    a. True
    b. False

22. Substances dissolved in a solution are referred to as *solutes*. (p. 68)
    a. True
    b. False

23. Homeostasis is the process whereby a protein molecule is broken down in the liver. (pp. 69, 70)
    a. True
    b. False

24. The glucose level in the mother's blood is higher than in the fetal blood. (p. 70)
    a. True
    b. False

25. High-molecular-weight (large-sized) proteins do not generally pass through the placenta. (p. 71)
    a. True
    b. False

Define

26. homeostasis (pp. 69, 70)
27. pinocytosis (p. 72)
28. facilitated diffusion (p. 70)
29. plasma membrane (p. 68)
30. polypeptide (p. 66)

31. peptide bond (p. 66)
32. phospholipid (p. 63)
33. hydrolysis (p. 63)
34. digestion (p. 63)

VOCABULARY

These are key words that you should know. By learning these words you achieve learning goal number 17. The text page where the respective definition occurs is indicated following the word.

1. monosaccharide (p. 62)
2. disaccharide (p. 62)
3. polysaccharide (p. 62)
4. digestion (p. 63)
5. glycogen (p. 63)
6. starch (p. 63)
7. fat (lipid) (p. 63)
8. fatty acids (p. 63)
9. glycerol (p. 63)
10. phospholipid (p. 63)
11. protein (pp. 63, 64)
12. amino acid (p. 64)
13. myosin, hemoglobin, and collagen (pp. 63, 64)
14. amino chemical group (p. 64)
15. carboxyl chemical group (p. 64)
16. general amino acid structure (p. 64)
17. peptide bond (p. 66)
18. polypeptide (p. 66)
19. semipermeable membrane (p. 68)
20. villus (pp. 66-68)
21. solute and solvent (p. 68)
22. diffusion (p. 68)
23. homeostasis (pp. 69, 70)
24. glycolysis (p. 70)
25. oxygen debt (p. 70)
26. carrier molecule (p. 70)
27. pinocytosis (p. 72)
28. gamma globulin (p. 72)
29. teratogens (p. 73)
30. salicylates (p. 73)
31. tissue rejection (p. 74)
32. paradoxical tolerance (p. 74)

STUDY EXERCISES

Instructions: Write out your answers carefully and completely on separate paper. Check your answers by referring to the text page indicated.

1. Briefly describe the general structure of carbohydrates, proteins, and fats. (pp. 61-64)
2. How is a fat molecule formed? (p. 63)
3. How do molecules pass from the maternal blood to the fetal blood? (pp. 66-68)
4. Why is a baby born of a diabetic mother generally heavier than normal? (p. 71)
5. What is catalyzed or facilitated diffusion? (p. 70)
6. What are some "good" biological reasons why every pregnancy should end in a physiological abortion (miscarriage)? (p. 74)

PROBE

1. Since medical science has knowledge that certain alterations in the maternal chemical environment represent potential dangers to the developing fetus, do you think:
   a. That all pregnant females should be warned of this by their physician? Specifically, do you think that cigarette smoking, alcohol, drugs, and viral infections should be explained to the prospective mother? (background p. 73)
   b. That if a child is detected to be deformed late in pregnancy, the mother should have the right to an abortion?

SELF-POSTTEST OF LEARNING GOALS

Instructions: After completing the vocabulary in written form it is now time to review. State each definition orally several times. Reread those areas in your text associated with the study exercises on which you did poorly. Retake the pretest at this time.

ANSWERS

1. a
2. e
3. c
4. a
5. d
6. a, c
7. c
8. d
9. a
10. a
11. c
12. d
13. b

14. carboxyl
15. glycine
16. polypeptide
17. 20
18. villi
19. glycolysis
20. Teratogens
21. a
22. a
23. b
24. a
25. a

Chapter 5

Fetal Development and Comparative Embryology

OVERVIEW

The human fetus exists under conditions totally different from those of the adult. Structurally, each system of the fetus reflects its dependence on the mother. As the fetus develops it does so in accord with its inherited potentialities. The fetus inherits more than just genetic instructions that direct its development from the parents. It cannot escape its ancestral heritage. There are several transitory structures that are clues to the relationship between the human fetus and an ancestral vertebrate stock. Despite the diversity of form and structure of various vertebrates, the embryos of all have many features in common and, in fact, share the same basic developmental pattern. Emphasis in this chapter will be placed on this vertebrate relationship, especially as it is associated with the cardiovascular and urogenital systems.

LEARNING GOALS

After successfully completing this chapter you should be able to do the following, orally or in writing.

1. State the principle of recapitulation.
2. Describe the embryonic vitelline circulation.
3. Describe the embryonic allantoic circulation.
4. Identify the chambers of the vertebrate heart.
5. Relate the embryonic role of the aortic arches.
6. Compare the stages of cardiovascular development in two vertebrates, the chick and human.
7. Describe pulmonary circulation in the vertebrate.
8. Use appropriately the vocabulary associated with this chapter when discussing its concepts.
9. Explain the process of "placental breathing."
10. Describe the ultimate fate of the foramen ovale and the ductus arteriosus.
11. Describe the embryonic development of the pronephros, mesonephros, and metanephros.
12. Discuss the differentiation of the reproductive organs.
13. Identify the cause of cryptorchism.
14. Describe the role of the sex chromosomes.
15. Discuss embryonic induction.
16. Relate how the brain of the male and female fetus reacts to testosterone.

SELF-PRETEST OF LEARNING GOALS

Before proceeding further in the study of this chapter, attempt to answer the following questions without referring to other information. Upon completion of the test, compare your responses with the answer key at the end of the *Study Guide* chapter. Then correct the wrong responses by referring to the text (page numbers are indicated following each question).

True—False

1. Structurally, each system of the fetus reflects its dependence on the mother. (p. 77)
   a. True   b. False

2. Darwin established the principle of recapitulation. (p. 77)
   a. True   b. False

3. All veins carry oxygen-poor blood. (p. 79)
   a. True   b. False

4. An artery is a blood vessel that carries blood away from the heart. (p. 79)
   a. True   b. False

5. The auricles are the chambers of the heart that collect blood returning from the body. (p. 79)
   a. True   b. False

6. The flow of blood to and from the organs and tissues constitutes the pulmonary circulation. (p. 80)
   a. True   b. False

Multiple Choice

7. When do the lungs normally become functional in the human fetus? (p. 86)
   a. 4th month   d. 8th month
   b. 6th month   e. 9th week
   c. 7th month   f. None of these

8. What structure in the fetus shunts blood from the pulmonary circulation directly into the aorta? (p. 85)
   a. Placenta   d. Spleen
   b. Lung   e. None of these
   c. Heart   f. Ductus arteriosus

9. What structure in the fetus substitutes for the lungs as the organ of gas exchange? (p. 85)
   a. Ductus arteriosus   d. Spleen
   b. Heart   e. None of these
   c. Placenta

10. The true kidney develops from which of the following? (p. 86)
    a. Placenta   d. Metanephros
    b. Pronephros   e. None of these
    c. Mesonephros   f. Ureter

11. When for some reason the testes do not descend into the enternal scrotum, the condition is known as (p. 88)
    a. cryptorchism.   d. Müllerianism.
    b. diabetes.   e. vasectomy.
    c. vaginitis.   f. none of these.

12. How many X chromosomes do genetic females possess? (p. 88)
    a. 1   d. 4
    b. 2   e. 0
    c. 3   f. 6

13. How many X chromosomes do genetic males possess? (p. 88)
    a. 1
    b. 2
    c. 3
    d. 4
    e. 0
    f. 6

14. What hormone is produced by the testes? (p. 89)
    a. FSH
    b. Thyroxine
    c. LH
    d. Testosterone
    e. None of these

15. What structure produces LH-releasing factor? (pp. 89, 90)
    a. Pituitary
    b. Hypothalamus
    c. Testis
    d. Ovary
    e. Kidney

VOCABULARY

These are key words that you should know. By learning these words you will achieve learning goal number 8. The page where the respective definition occurs is indicated following the word or group of words.

 1. fetal circulatory system (p. 77)
 2. ontogeny (p. 78)
 3. phylogeny (p. 78)
 4. vitelline circulation (p. 79)
 5. allantoic circulation (p. 79)
 6. auricle (p. 79)
 7. ventricle (p. 79)
 8. aortic arches (p. 79)
 9. cardinal veins (p. 80)
10. oxidation (p. 83)
11. deoxygenated (p. 81)
12. ductus arteriosus (p. 85)
13. foramen ovale (p. 85)
14. pronephros (p. 86)
15. mesonephros (p. 86)
16. metanephros (p. 86)
17. ligamentum arteriosum (p. 86)
18. Wolffian ducts (p. 86)
19. Müllerian ducts (p. 87)
20. cryptorchism (p. 88)
21. gonad (p. 87)
22. sex chromosomes (p. 88)
23. external genitalia (p. 89)
24. induction (p. 89)
25. hypothalamus (p. 89)
26. testosterone (p. 90)

STUDY EXERCISES

Instructions: Write out your answers carefully and completely on a separate paper. Check your answers by referring to the text page indicated.

1. Briefly state the principle of recapitulation. (pp. 77, 78)
2. How does the intraembryonic circulation allow the fetus to receive oxygen and nutrients? (pp. 79-81)
3. Describe pulmonary circulation. (p. 82)
4. Compare the embryonic development of the cardiovascular system of the amphibian, reptile, bird, and mammal. (pp. 81-85)
5. Briefly describe the changes at birth of placenta (fetal) circulation. (pp. 85, 86)
6. Explain how the human excretory system reflects an ancestral heritage. (pp. 86, 87)
7. Describe the process whereby the ovaries and the testes undergo differentiation during embryonic development. (pp. 87-89)
8. Explain cryptorchism. (p. 88)
9. How do males and females differ? Compare them with respect to their sex chromosomes. (pp. 88, 89)

PROBE

1. Based on the type of research data presented on pages 89 and 90, do you think that the ability to control the sex of the fetus will ever become a reality?
2. Once again, but now after five chapters, when do you think life begins? Is it at fertilization, implantation, three months, etc.?

SELF-POSTTEST OF LEARNING GOALS

Instructions: After completing the vocabulary in written form it is now time to review. State each definition orally several times. Reread those areas in your text associated with the study exercises on which you did poorly. Retake the pretest at this time.

ANSWERS

1. a	9. c
2. b	10. d
3. b	11. a
4. a	12. b
5. a	13. a
6. b	14. d
7. f	15. b
8. f	

Chapter 6

Organization of the Developing Egg

OVERVIEW

A vexing problem that has long occupied the mind of scientists and laymen alike is the extent to which the developing embryo is irreversibly "programmed." How does the embryo "know" what to do next? How does a fertilized egg progressively develop into a species-copy of its parents? This chapter presents material that allows you to follow the chronology of the early development of the fertilized egg. Included in this discussion is the spontaneous twinning in humans resulting in either dizygotic (fraternal) twins or monozygotic (identical) twins. Lastly, the entire process of development is unfolded, thus allowing you to observe that genes in the nucleus prescribe the potentialities for the structures that are to emerge. In fact, the code established in the zygote (fertilized egg) is the same until death, barring mutations.

LEARNING GOALS

After successfully completing this chapter you should be able to do the following, orally or in writing.

1. Present the early history associated with the organization of the egg.
2. State the process of epigenesis and relate it to the modern theory of the organization of the egg.
3. Briefly describe the investigations of Driesch and Hörstadius concerning the development of the fertilized egg.
4. Relate cleavage to the normal change in the fertilized egg.
5. Discuss the cell types present in the 64-cell stage of the sea urchin egg.
6. Describe the process of gastrulation.
7. Relate the formation of the germ layers to tissue differentiation.
8. Formulate arguments for or against the double gradient theory.
9. Use appropriately the vocabulary associated with this chapter when discussing its concepts.
10. Explain how, embryologically, human fraternal (dizygotic) and identical (monozygotic) twins emerge.

SELF-PRETEST OF LEARNING GOALS

Before proceeding further, attempt to answer the following questions. Pretests are designed to act as indicators of specific areas of subject weakness. Review your incorrect answers by referring to the text (page numbers are given following each question). Answers are provided at the end of the *Study Guide* chapter.

Matching

1. Driesch (p. 93)
2. Runnström (p. 97)
3. Spemann (p. 99)
4. Mintz (p. 103)

a. conceived embryo as equipotential system
b. none of these
c. postulated existence of organizing centers
d. studied constricted fertilized egg
e. developed quadriparental embryo

Multiple Choice

5. Who developed the doctrine of vitalism? (p. 94)
   a. Driesch
   b. Runnström
   c. Spemann
   d. Mintz
   e. None of these

6. The early cell divisions of the zygote are termed (p. 95)
   a. blastula.
   b. gastrula.
   c. cleavage.
   d. none of these.
   e. micophores.

7. As cell division continues the cells of the embryo become arranged in the form of a hollow ball and the embryo is now known as the (p. 96)
   a. blastula.
   b. gastrula.
   c. fetus.
   d. none of these.
   e. archenteron.

8. The outer cell layer of the gastrula is called (p. 97)
   a. blastula.
   b. archenteron.
   c. ectoderm.
   d. none of these.
   e. endoderm.

9. How many germ layers are there? (p. 97)
   a. One
   b. Two
   c. Three
   d. Four
   e. Five

True—False

10. Identical twins are said to be monozygotic. (p. 100)
    a. True
    b. False

11. The animal half of the embryo shows distinct developmental differences from the vegetal half. (p. 94)
    a. True
    b. False

12. The fertilized egg first increases its surface by dividing into small cells. (p. 95)
    a. True
    b. False

13. When the cell reaches the 32-cell stage, the animal half has two rings of 8 cells. (p. 95)
    a. True
    b. False

14. During gastrulation cells push in one side of the ball-shaped embryo. This inpushing is called *invagination.* (p. 97)
    a. True
    b. False

15. The mesoderm is the middle germ layer. (p. 97)
    a. True
    b. False

16. Runnström postulated the existence of organizing centers in embryo cells. (p. 97)
    a. True
    b. False

17. The terms *fraternal* and *dizygotic* are synonymous. (p. 100)
    a. True
    b. False

VOCABULARY

These are key words or phrases that you should know. By learning these you will achieve learning goal number 9. The page where the respective definition occurs is indicated following the word or phrase.

1. epigenesis (p. 93)
2. equipotential (pp. 93, 94)
3. presumptive fate (p. 94)
4. embryo (animal-half cells) (pp. 94, 95)
5. embryo (vegetal-half cells) (pp. 94, 95)
6. cleavage (p. 95)
7. mesomere, macromere, and micromere (pp. 95, 96)
8. blastula and blastocoel (p. 96)
9. gastrula and gastrulation (p. 97)
10. ectoderm, endoderm, and mesoderm (p. 97)
11. archenteron and blastopore (p. 97)
12. labile system (p. 98)
13. gray crescent (p. 98)
14. fraternal or dizygotic twins (p. 100)
15. identical or monozygotic twins (p. 100)
16. zona pellucida (pp. 103, 104)

STUDY EXERCISES

Instructions: Write out your answers carefully and completely on a separate paper. Check your answers by referring back to the text page indicated.

1. What is epigenesis? How does it relate to the modern theory of the organization of the egg? (pp. 93-100)
2. Describe the early investigations of Hans Driesch as they relate to the development of the fertilized egg. (pp. 93-95)
3. Describe the sequence of events that occurs immediately after the egg is fertilized and terminates with the formation of the gastrula (gastrulation). (pp. 95-97)
4. Explain the double gradient theory. (p. 97-98)
5. What contribution did Hans Spemann make to the field of early embryonic development? (pp. 99, 100)
6. What is the difference between dizygotic and monozygotic twins? (p. 100)

PROBE

1. Do you feel that embryologists should be allowed to use living human egg and sperm cells to observe fertilization and cleavage?

SELF-POSTTEST OF LEARNING GOALS

Instructions: After completing the vocabulary in written form it is now time to review. State each definition orally several times. Reread those areas in your text associated with the study questions on which you did poorly. Retake the pretest at this time.

ANSWERS

1. a
2. c
3. d
4. e
5. a
6. c
7. a
8. c
9. c
10. a
11. a
12. a
13. a
14. a
15. a
16. a
17. a

Chapter 7

Differentiation and the Organizer

OVERVIEW

The developing embryo is a unique mass of cells. The sum of the different developmental possibilities of the cell in early division exceeds the eventual destiny of that cell in the normal developmental process. One of the very early characteristics of the developing embryonic cells is specialization. The germ tissues (ectoderm, mesoderm, and endoderm) begin to differentiate into specialized structures such as muscle, bone, brain, and heart. This chapter presents materials concerned with the process of differentiation in various vertebrate animals. Special emphasis is placed on why the crucial period of development in the human occurs prior to the eighth week of pregnancy.

LEARNING GOALS

After successfully completing this chapter you should, orally or in writing, be able to do the following.

1. Describe the process of embryonic development in the frog *(Rana pipiens)*.
2. Discuss the phenomenon of epiboly.
3. Describe the formation of the notochord.
4. State the results of Vogt's experimentation.
5. Use appropriately the vocabulary associated with this chapter when discussing the concepts presented.
6. Describe the formation of somites in the embryo.
7. Differentiate between the various types of mesoderm tissue.
8. Discuss the result of the research performed by Spemann and Mangold as it relates to the dorsal lip of the blastopore.
9. Describe the embryonic role of the organizer.
10. Relate the process of induction to the role of the organizer.
11. Describe the current "turned on" gene theory as it relates to induction.
12. Discuss the experimentation of Oscar Schotté.
13. State the effect of thalidomide on limb formation of the human embryo.
14. Describe some of the developmental abnormalities that may result should a pregnant woman contract German measles.

SELF-PRETEST OF LEARNING GOALS

Before proceeding further in the study of this chapter, attempt to answer the following questions without referring to other information. Upon completion of the test, compare your responses with the answer key at the end of the *Study Guide* chapter. Then correct the wrong responses by referring to the text (page numbers are indicated following each question).

Multiple Choice

1. When cleavage of an egg occurs such that the entire egg mass is divided, the type of division is termed (p. 107)
   a. holoblastic.
   b. octagonal.
   c. blastophoric.
   d. gastrophoric.

2. In which hemisphere is the blastocoel located? (p. 107)
   a. Animal
   b. Vegetal

3. In which hemisphere is the yolk plug located? (p. 110)
   a. Animal
   b. Vegetal

4. The primitive gut is also known as the (p. 110)
   a. yolk plug.
   b. blastocoel.
   c. archenteron.
   d. gastrophore.

5. The downward movement of cells during gastrulation that result in the envelopment of the yolk-laden cells of the vegetal hemisphere are known as (p. 110)
   a. holoblastic.
   b. epiboly.
   c. blastophoric.
   d. gastrophoric.

6. The cells just in front of the dorsal lip of the blastopore become the (p. 110)
   a. archenteron.
   b. yolk plug.
   c. notochord.
   d. blastocoel.

7. The cells to the left and right of the dorsal lip become the (p. 110)
   a. archenteron.
   b. notochord.
   c. mesoderm.
   d. yolk plug.

Fill in the Blank

8. The ingrowth of cells, or the inward movement of cells at the blastopore lips, is referred to as _____. (p. 110)

9. The _____ tube is the embryonic forerunner of the adult spinal cord. (pp. 111-113)

10. Because of experimentation by _____ a fate map was constructed. (p. 111)

11. The central portion of the chordamesoderm differentiates as a solid rod of cells known as the _____. (p. 113)

12. The dorsal mesoderm divides transversely into components known as _____. (p. 113)

True—False

13. The risk of damage to the human fetus from the virus causing German measles is almost wholly during the first three months of pregnancy. (p. 120)
    a. True
    b. False

14. The earlier in human pregnancy that German measles occurs, the greater the changes of injury to the infant. (p. 120)
    a. True
    b. False

15. Because of its property of organizing the ectoderm into nervous tissue, the chordamesoderm is termed the *organizer*. (p. 115)
    a. True
    b. False

16. The drug thalidomide causes brain malformation in the developing human fetus. (pp. 119, 120)
    a. True
    b. False

Matching

17. Spemann
18. Vogt
19. Mangold
20. Holtfreter

    a. Nobel prize recipient for organizer research (p. 115)
    b. fate map construction (p. 111)
    c. fixed region of gastrula (p. 113)
    d. tested tissue to determine induction of neural development (p. 117)

VOCABULARY

These are key words that you should know. By learning these words you will achieve learning goal number 5. The page where the respective definition occurs is indicated following the word.

1. differentiation (p. 107)
2. holoblastic (p. 107)
3. blastocoel (p. 107)
4. blastula (p. 107)
5. gastrulation (pp. 108, 109)
6. blastopore (p. 109)
7. dorsal lip (blastopore) (p. 110)
8. yolk plug (p. 110)
9. archenteron (p. 110)
10. epiboly (p. 110)
11. involution (p. 110)
12. notochord (p. 110)
13. epidermal ectoderm (p. 111)
14. neural plate ectoderm (p. 111)
15. neural tube (pp. 111-113)
16. neural folds (p. 113)
17. somite (p. 113)
18. coelom (p. 113)
19. organizer (p. 115)
20. induction (p. 115)
21. thalidomide (p. 119)
22. German measles (p. 120)

STUDY EXERCISES

Instructions: Write out your answers carefully and completely on a separate paper. Check your answers by referring to the text page indicated.

1. Briefly describe the formation of the notochord. (pp. 110, 113)
2. Discuss the concepts concerning the role of the organizer. (pp. 115-117)
3. Briefly state the role of the inducer. (p. 117)

PROBE

1. Present arguments for and/or against whether the general public should be alerted to the effects of various drugs and chemicals on the developing fetus.
2. Should a human female contract German measles at approximately five weeks of pregnancy, what would you recommend?
3. Based on the comparison of various animals through the first seven chapters of your text, would you accept embryonic research data compiled from a salamander or frog as being comparable to human embryonic development? To go a step further, if a selected chemical caused an embryonic cell malfunction in the frog, would you expect essentially the same result in the human (based on the same stage of development in each, such as the first one-third or one-half of development)?

SELF-POSTTEST OF LEARNING GOALS

Instructions: After completing the vocabulary in written form it is now time to review. State each definition orally several times. Reread those areas in your text associated with the study exercises on which you did poorly. Retake the pretest at this time.

ANSWERS

1. a
2. a
3. a
4. c
5. b
6. c
7. c
8. involution
9. neural
10. Vogt

11. notochord
12. somites
13. a
14. a
15. a
16. b
17. a
18. b
19. c
20. d

Chapter 8

Problem of Nuclear Differentiation

OVERVIEW

The ultimate result of the union of a single egg and sperm is a living, breathing being composed of literally billions of cells. Visualize, if you will, that two single sex cells come together, divide into two cells, these two into four, and so on. Eventually, these cells begin to differentiate into tissue types such as nervous, muscle, blood, bone, and others. Every cell is programmed through its genes. These genes, in the form of specific DNA arrangements, are passed from cell to cell as division and differentiation occur. A better understanding of the role and structure of the gene in the nucleus may result in the ability of science to manipulate the heredity of the individual. This would definitely be an advantage when specific DNA arrangements result in embryonic or childhood defects and malfunctions. This chapter presents material associated with experimental endeavors concerning the cell nucleus.

LEARNING GOALS

After successfully completing this chapter you should, orally or in writing, be able to do the following.

1. Describe the action of the nucleus during various phases of development.
2. Discuss the "cap-forming" concept as stated by Hämmerling.
3. Relate the findings of Briggs and King as they apply to the role of the nucleus in embryonic development.
4. Describe the result of the work done by Moore as it relates to nuclear-cytoplasmic feedback.
5. Discuss the postulate of Gurdon concerning differential gene action.
6. State the findings of Gurdon and Brown as they relate to nuclear reversibility.
7. Describe differential gene action.
8. State an opinion about the formation of a human clone.
9. Use appropriately the vocabulary associated with this chapter when discussing the concepts presented.

SELF-PRETEST OF LEARNING GOALS

Before proceeding further in the study of this chapter, attempt to answer the following questions without referring to other information. Upon completion of the test, compare your responses with the answer key at the end of the *Study Guide* chapter. Then correct the wrong responses by referring to the text (page numbers are indicated following each question).

True—False

1. From a single zygote, the fertilized egg, all tissue types will develop. (p. 123)
   a. True   b. False

2. Every cell in the plant or animal contains the full complement of genes. (p. 123)
   a. True   b. False

3. Research by Gurdon has demonstrated that certain genes in the cell nucleus remain inactive until activated. (p. 130)
   a. True   b. False

4. There is strong evidence for a reversible change in the activity of a cell nucleus. (p. 131)
   a. True   b. False

Matching

5. Roux (p. 123)
6. Hämmerling (p. 123)
7. Briggs and King (pp. 124-127)
8. Moore (p. 129)
9. Gurdon (p. 130)
10. Gurdon and Brown (p. 131)

a. used alga to show nuclear control over development
b. nuclear transplantation irreversibility
c. studied nuclear cytoplasmic feedback
d. none of these
e. postulated determinants for differentiation
f. repressed RNA

VOCABULARY

These are key words that you should know. By learning these words you will achieve learning goal number 9. The page where the respective definition occurs is indicated following the word.

1. differential gene action (p. 132)   2. clone (pp. 132, 133)

STUDY EXERCISES

Instructions: Write out your answers carefully and completely on a separate paper. Check your answers by referring to the text page indicated.

1. Describe, briefly, research that indicates the nucleus controls developmental processes. (pp. 123-132)
2. What was the basic conclusion drawn from the research by Hämmerling? (pp. 123)
3. Describe serial transplantation as stated by Briggs and King. (pp. 127, 128)
4. What is nuclear cytoplasmic feedback? (pp. 129, 130)
5. After analyzing the material in this chapter, present arguments for or against permanent gene inactivation. (pp. 130, 131)

PROBE

1. Based on materials presented at the end of this chapter, present arguments for or against the establishment of a human clone.
2. Would you, as a parent, prefer the choice of selecting basic characteristics (IQ, eye color, height, etc.) of your offspring?

SELF-POSTTEST OF LEARNING GOALS

Instructions: After completing the vocabulary in written form it is now time to review. State each definition orally several times. Reread those areas in your text associated with the study exercises on which you did poorly. Retake the pretest at this time.

ANSWERS

1. a
2. a
3. a
4. a
5. e

6. a
7. b
8. c
9. d
10. f

Chapter 9

Hybrid Embryos and Cellular Metabolism

OVERVIEW

The activity of the gene during embryonic development is not totally understood. We do know that every step in development and metabolism is controlled by an enzyme. All enzymes are protein and produced via a very selective gene-ribosome system. The ribosome is a cell part (organelle) that is associated with protein production (synthesis). Enzymes affect the rates of chemical reactions that occur in the plant or animal cell. Generally, a cellular chemical reaction involves a rearrangement of the atoms of molecules. During development the cellular metabolic patterns for enzyme production, energy utilization, and cell duplication are initiated. This chapter will present materials that will allow you to follow the pathways that many researchers have trod in an attempt to unravel the mysteries of the chemistry of development.

LEARNING GOALS

After successfully completing this chapter you should, orally or in writing, be able to do the following.

1. Describe cellular respiration by utilizing the embryonic cell as a model.
2. Discuss the role of glucose as the main energy source for cellular metabolism.
3. State the fate of glucose in glycolysis.
4. Describe the production of a hybrid embryo.
5. Correlate the presence of glucose and the production of energy.
6. Use appropriately the vocabulary associated with this chapter when discussing the concepts presented.
7. Identify the structure of ATP.
8. Specify the role of ATP as the cell's carrier of chemical energy.
9. Describe a chemical reaction in the cell.
10. Discuss the activity of an enzyme as it relates to the substrate.
11. Specify the role of the coenzyme in cellular metabolism.
12. Differentiate between aerobic and anaerobic respiration.
13. Describe the process of glycolysis as it relates to the Krebs cycle.
14. Discuss the energy transfer that occurs as a result of the Krebs cycle.
15. Describe the role of oxygen.
16. Discuss the formation of urea during protein breakdown.
17. Relate the typical energy-producing pathways that occur in the cell to those of the hybrid embryo.

SELF-PRETEST OF LEARNING GOALS

Before proceeding further in the study of this chapter, attempt to answer the following questions without referring to other information. Upon completion of the test, compare your responses with the answer key at the end of the *Study Guide* chapter. Then correct the wrong responses by referring to the text (page numbers are indicated following each question).

True—False

1. The sum total of chemical reactions that occur in a living system is known as *metabolism*. (p. 137)
   a. True b. False

2. Glucose in virtually all animals is the main energy source. (p. 139)
   a. True b. False

3. Glycolysis is the conversion of glycogen to glucose. (p. 139)
   a. True b. False

4. Energy is the capacity to do work. (p. 140)
   a. True b. False

5. Glucose, when burned, liberates 36 molecules of energy. (p. 150)
   a. True b. False

6. All enzymes contain at least one coenzyme. (p. 143)
   a. True b. False

Multiple Choice

7. Glycolysis involves the breakdown of glucose to (p. 139)
   a. glycogen.
   b. water.
   c. pyruvic acid.
   d. none of these.

8. The energy of motion is known as (p. 140)
   a. potential.
   b. kinetic.
   c. active.
   d. none of these.

9. Heat is measured in units of (p. 140)
   a. calories.
   b. grams.
   c. ergs.
   d. none of these.

10. What process enables the green plant to store the energy of sunlight within organic compounds? (p. 141)
    a. Glycolysis
    b. Photosynthesis
    c. Krebs cycle
    d. None of these

11. The living cell is able to capture approximately what percent of the released energy from a glucose molecule? (p. 141)
    a. 55
    b. 80
    c. 20
    d. 10
    e. 100
    f. 30

12. ATP consists of which of the following compounds? (p. 141)
    a. Adenine, ribose, and phosphate
    b. Glucose, adenine, and phosphate
    c. Glucose, glycogen, and phosphate
    d. None of these

Fill in the Blanks

13. Reactions involving phosphate, particularly the formation of ATP from ADP, are called _____. (p. 142)

14. When glucose is oxidized the energy released from the carbon-hydrogen bonds of glucose is trapped to form _____. (p. 142)

15. Most vitamins taken into the animal body are converted to _____. (p. 143)

16. NAD is derived from the vitamin _____. (p. 144)

17. The conversion of glucose to pyruvic acid is known as _____ (pp. 139, 145)

18. When oxygen is deficient or lacking during glycolysis _____ acid is formed. (p. 145)

19. _____ organisms survive in the total absence of oxygen. (pp. 146, 147)

20. Coenzyme A is a derivative of _____ acid, one of the B vitamins. (p. 147)

21. The citric acid cycle is also known as the _____ cycle. (p. 148)

22. Each molecule of glucose ultimately produces _____ molecules of ATP. (p. 150)

23. The end production of protein breakdown is ammonia (NH_3), which is converted to _____ , a compound readily excreted in the urine. (p. 152)

VOCABULARY

These are key words that you should know. By learning these words you will achieve learning goal number 6. The page where the respective definition occurs is indicated following the word.

1. metabolism (p. 137)
2. glycolysis (p. 139)
3. energy (p. 140)
4. potential energy (p. 140)
5. kinetic energy (p. 140)
6. calorie (p. 140)
7. photosynthesis (p. 141)
8. ATP (p. 141)
9. ADP (p. 141)
10. phosphorylation (p. 142)
11. enzyme (p. 142)
12. chemical reaction (p. 142)
13. substrate (p. 143)
14. coenzyme (p. 143)
15. vitamin (pp. 143, 144)
16. NAD and FAD (pp. 144 and 148)
17. pyruvic acid (pp. 145-148)
18. alcoholic fermentation (p. 147)
19. Krebs cycle (p. 148)
20. electron transport system (p. 150)
21. respiration (p. 150)
22. urea (p. 152)

STUDY EXERCISES

Instructions: Write out your answers carefully and completely on a separate paper. Check your answers by referring to the text page indicated.

1. How do you produce a hybrid embryo? (p. 137)
2. Briefly describe the process of glycolysis, the formation of acetyl coenzyme A, and the Krebs cycle. (pp. 145-149)
3. What compounds comprise the structure of ATP? (p. 141)
4. Describe how ATP acts as the cell's carrier of chemical energy. (pp. 142, 145-151)
5. What is a coenzyme? (p. 143)
6. How does an enzyme-substrate system operate? (p. 143)
7. What is the role of oxygen in cellular respiration? (p. 150)
8. What is the origin of urea? (p. 152)

SELF-POSTTEST OF LEARNING GOALS

Instructions: After completing the vocabulary in written form it is now time to review. State each definition orally several times. Reread those areas in your text associated with the study exercises on which you did poorly. Retake the pretest at this time.

ANSWERS

1. a
2. a
3. b
4. a
5. b
6. b
7. c
8. b
9. a
10. b
11. a
12. a

13. phosphorylation
14. ATP
15. coenzymes
16. niacin
17. glycolysis
18. lactic
19. anaerobic
20. panothenic
21. Krebs
22. 38
23. urea

Chapter 10

Cell Structure and Function

OVERVIEW

All organ systems are composed of tissues. All tissues are composed of cells and all cells are composed of organelles (parts). As our instrumentation and knowledge have increased, we now draw a different picture of the cell than we did 20 or even 10 years ago. It was the advent of the electron microscope and the refinement of techniques utilized in the laboratory that enabled the great advancements of the past several decades. Rather than speak of what this cell does or that cell does we now are able to define the exact role of a cell organelle, such as the ribosome, mitochondria, or lysosome. This chapter details the structure and interrelated chemical functions of the various cell organelles. It is imperative to gain a workable knowledge of how the organelles of a cell function, for without it the ability to understand how the organ system operates may escape you.

LEARNING GOALS

After successfully completing this chapter you should, orally or in writing, be able to do the following.

1. Relate developments of the past several decades that have allowed the advancement of knowledge in the field of cell biology.
2. Describe the historical aspects of the cell.
3. Discuss the structure and function of the mitochondria.
4. State the association between the endoplasmic reticulum (ER) and the ribosome.
5. Describe the function of the ribosome.
6. Differentiate between the function of smooth-surfaced and rough-surfaced endoplasmic reticular membranes.
7. State the function of the Golgi apparatus.
8. Discuss the relationships between protein synthesis, the ER, the Golgi apparatus, and protein secretion.
9. Describe the normal activity of the lysosomes.
10. Discuss the general structure of the nucleus.
11. Describe the structure of the cell membrane.
12. Differentiate between procaryotic and eucaryotic cells.
13. Briefly describe the evolution of the various cell organelles.
14. Use appropriately the vocabulary of this chapter as it relates to concepts presented.

SELF-PRETEST OF LEARNING GOALS

Before proceeding further in the study of this chapter, attempt to answer the following questions without referring to other information. Upon completion of the test, compare your responses with the answer key at the end of the *Study Guide* chapter. Then correct the wrong responses by referring to the text (page numbers are indicated following each question).

Matching

1. Hooke (p. 158)
2. van Leeuwenhoek (pp. 158, 159)
3. Purkinje (p. 159)
4. Brown (p. 159)
5. Schleiden and Schwann (p. 159)

a. observed cork and coined the term *cellula*
b. defined the fluid area of the cell as *protoplasm*
c. normalized the use of the word *nucleus*
d. Dutch lens grinder who observed pond water and called what he saw *animacules*
e. formulated the cell theory

Matching

6. Mitochondria (pp. 161, 162)
7. Ribosome (p. 164)
8. Golgi apparatus (pp. 164, 165)
9. Lysosome (p. 166)
10. Endoplasmic reticulum (pp. 163, 164)
11. Nucleus (pp. 167, 168)
12. Nucleolus (p. 168)

a. flattened membranes housing ribosomes
b. ATP is packaged here
c. collects and packages protein for export
d. houses DNA
e. plays a dominant role in protein synthesis
f. digests large molecules without causing damage to the cell
g. site of certain RNA synthesis

Matching

13. Mitochondria (p. 161)
14. Endoplasmic reticulum (pp. 163, 164)
15. Lysosome (p. 166)
16. Nucleus (pp. 167, 168)
17. Cell membrane (p. 168)

a. network of interconnected membranous sheets with channels between the sheets
b. cylindrical-shaped body bounded by a double-walled membrane
c. chromosomes composed of DNA are found here
d. membrane segregates lytic enzymes from the rest of cell, so that the cell will not be attacked by its own enzymes
e. triple-layered such that a biomolecular layer of lipid is between two outer monolayers of protein

True—False

18. The advent of the electron microscope in the late 1960s allowed scientists to see the detailed structure of the mitochondria for the first time. (p. 158)
    a. True   b. False

19. The inner membrane of the mitochondria is extended into numerous folds or projections known as *cristae.* (p.161)
    a. True   b. False

20. The terminal stage in the breakdown of glucose provides the cell with 95 percent of the ATP synthesized from glucose breakdown. (p. 162)
    a. True   b. False

21. The enzymes necessary for each step in the Krebs cycle are snythesized in the ribosomes. (p. 164)
    a. True   b. False

22. Glycolysis occurs in the mitochondria. (p. 162)
    a. True   b. False

23. Keith Porter first described the endoplasmic reticulum. (p. 163)
   a. True
   b. False

24. The endoplasmic reticulum furnishes a means of communication between the nucleus and the cytoplasm. (pp. 163, 164)
   a. True
   b. False

25. A lysosome that has not yet participated in its act of digestion is termed a *phagosome*. (p. 166)
   a. True
   b. False

26. The nucleus is enclosed by a porous double membrane. (p. 168)
   a. True
   b. False

27. The cell membrane is also known as the *plasma membrane*. (p. 168)
   a. True
   b. False

VOCABULARY

These are key words that you should know. By learning these you will achieve learning goal 14. The page where the respective definition occurs is indicated following the word.

1. cell organelle (p. 157)
2. mitochondria (pp. 161, 162)
3. cristae (p. 161)
4. matrix (p. 161)
5. endoplasmic reticulum (pp. 163-165)
6. ribosome (p. 164)
7. Golgi apparatus (pp. 164, 165)
8. lysosome (p. 166)
9. phagosome (p. 166)
10. chromatin (pp. 167, 168)
11. nucleolus (p. 168)
12. cell membrane (p. 168)
13. procaryotic cell (p. 169)
14. eucaryotic cell (p. 169)
15. zymogen (p. 170)

STUDY EXERCISES

Instructions: Write out your answers carefully and completely on a separate paper. Check your answers by referring to the text page indicated.

1. Differentiate between procaryotic and eucaryotic cells. (p. 169)
2. What are the major factors that have contributed to the recent accumulation of knowledge in the field of cell biology? (pp. 158-160)
3. What is the basic difference between smooth (agranular) and rough (granular) endoplasmic reticulum? (p. 164)
4. Briefly describe the functional relationships between protein synthesis, the endoplasmic reticulum, the Golgi apparatus, and protein secretion. (pp. 163-166)
5. Describe briefly the evolution of the various cell organelles. (pp. 169, 170)

SELF-POSTTEST OF LEARNING GOALS

Instructions: After completing the vocabulary in written form it is now time to review. State each definition orally several times. Reread those areas in your text associated with the study exercises on which you did poorly. Retake the pretest at this time.

ANSWERS

1. a
2. d
3. b
4. c
5. e
6. b
7. e
8. c
9. f
10. a
11. d
12. g
13. b

14. a
15. d
16. c
17. e
18. b
19. a
20. a
21. a
22. b
23. a
24. a
25. b
26. a
27. a

Chapter 11

Metabolism at the Organismal Level

OVERVIEW

The plant and animal cell is in reality a very active metabolic unit. It is continually building up (anabolism) and tearing down (catabolism) molecules. The cell is able to maintain a unique balance between anabolism and catabolism. Thus we have molecules as the structural units of the cell organelle. The cell organelles collectively are known as the *cell*. Cells with similar function are called *tissues*. Lastly, tissues with essentially the same function are known as *organs* or *organ systems*. It is imperative that you realize that in higher animals all organ systems function together. Each system has a unique role to perform, so that the organism maintains the balance that represents life. This chapter presents how these specialized systems in man are totally integrated. It is this integration that allows you to realize the total dependence of one system on another.

LEARNING GOALS

After successfully completing this chapter you should, orally or in writing, be able to do the following.

 1. Describe the anatomy (structure) of the mammalian digestive system.
 2. Discuss the digestive activity that occurs in the stomach following the ingestion of a meal.
 3. Describe the process of digestion after chyme (acidified food) leaves the stomach.
 4. State the role of the pancreas in digestion.
 5. Discuss the site of bile production, the storage of bile, and the role of bile in digestion.
 6. Describe the function of the large intestine seqment in digestion.
 7. Discuss the general structure of the mammalian circulatory and lymphatic systems.
 8. Describe the role of the liver as a part of the circulatory system.
 9. Relate how edema may occur.
10. Discuss the components of blood.
11. Describe the structure of the mammalian respiratory system.
12. Discuss the role of the alveolus.
13. Describe the structure of the mammalian excretory system.
14. Discuss the process of filtration and reabsorption.
15. Describe how waste utilization occurs on this planet.
16. Use appropriately the vocabulary of this chapter as it relates to concepts presented.

SELF-PRETEST OF LEARNING GOALS

Before proceeding further in the study of this chapter, attempt to answer the following questions without referring to other information. Upon completion of the test, compare your responses with the answer key at the end of the *Study Guide* chapter. Then correct the wrong responses by referring to the text (page numbers are indicated following each question).

Fill in the Blank

1. All the chemical reactions occurring in the cell are known collectively as _____. (p. 175)

2. Pepsin is produced by the _____ . (p. 177)

3. The longest segment of the small intestine is known as the _____ . (p. 179)

4. The tube that connects the pharynx to the stomach is the _____ . (p. 176)

5. The muscle that controls the flow of food from the stomach to the duodenum is the _____ sphincter. (p. 179)

6. Bile is produced by the _____ . (p. 179)

7. The major bile pigment is _____ . (p. 182)

8. The largest artery of the body is the _____ aorta. (p. 182)

9. The smallest blood vessels are the _____ . (p. 182)

10. The _____ arteries supply blood to the neck and head. (p. 182)

11. The contraction of the ventricles forces blood to the lung via the _____ arteries. (p. 184)

12. Materials (other than fat) absorbed in the small intestine pass to the liver via the _____ _____ vein. (p. 184)

13. When amino acids are broken down the process is known as _____ . (p. 185)

14. When amino acids are broken down the formation of toxic ammonia occurs, but the ammonia is rapidly changed to _____ . (p. 185)

Matching

15. Neutrophil (p. 187)
16. Platelet (p. 187)
17. Erythrocyte (p. 187)
18. Leucocyte (p. 187)
19. Lymphocyte (p. 187)

a. another term for red blood cell
b. specific type of white blood cell
c. none of these
d. another term for white blood cell
e. has a role in blood clotting

Matching

20. Larynx (p. 187)
21. Parotid (p. 175)
22. Pancreas (p. 179)
23. Duodenum (p. 179)
24. Glottis (p. 177)

a. salivary gland
b. shortest portion of small intestine
c. voice box
d. releases digestive enzymes
e. opening between vocal cords

Multiple Choice

25. Which of the following is not a salivary gland? (p. 175)
    a. Parotid
    b. Submaxillary
    c. Glottis
    d. Sublingual

26. Blood enters the kidney through what artery? (p. 189)
   a. Carotid
   b. Coronary
   c. Renal
   d. Vena cava

27. The filtration process of the kidney actually occurs in microscopic units known as (p. 189)
   a. nephrons.
   b. glottis.
   c. veriformix.
   d. caecum.

28. Each of the microscopic units mentioned in question 27 contains a tuft of capillaries known as the (p. 189)
   a. nephron.
   b. Bowman's capsule.
   c. glomerulus.
   d. glottis.

29. Which of the following would not be filtered from the capillary in Bowman's capsule? (p. 189)
   a. Glucose
   b. Water
   c. Potassium ions
   d. Red blood cells

30. The trachea divides (bifurcates) into (p. 187)
   a. alveoli.
   b. bronchiole.
   c. larynx.
   d. bronchi.

31. Malfunctioning of the lymphatic mechanism can result in a swelling of tissues known as (p. 185)
   a. lymphocytoma.
   b. edema.
   c. jaundice.
   d. leucopenia.

32. When food becomes acidified by the action of hydrochloric acid it (the food) becomes known as (p. 179)
   a. casein.
   b. rennin.
   c. chyme.
   d. flatus.
   e. bilin.

33. The numerous fingerlike projections of the small intestine are known as (p. 180)
   a. cecum.
   b. villi.
   c. lacteals.
   d. colonii.

Matching (Select the appropriate answer or answers.)

34. Erythrocytes (p. 187)
35. Leucocytes (p. 187)
36. Glucose (pp. 181, 184, 189)
37. Water (pp. 180, 182, 189)
38. Urea (pp. 185, 189)

a. normally found in blood
b. normally found in urine
c. normally found in feces
d. normally found in chyme

VOCABULARY

These are key words that you should know. By learning these words you will achieve learning goal 16. The page where the respective definition occurs is indicated following the word.

1. metabolism (p. 175)
2. catabolism (p. 175)
3. anabolism (p. 175)
4. salivary glands (p. 175)
5. taste buds (p. 175)
6. salivary amylase (p. 175)
7. pharynx (p. 176)
8. esophagus (p. 176)
9. peristaltic waves (p. 176)
10. starch (pp. 175, 176)
11. maltose (p. 176)
12. glottis (p. 177)

13. gastric juice (p. 177)
14. heartburn (p. 177)
15. peptic ulcer (p. 179)
16. chyme (p. 179)
17. small intestine (p. 179)
18. pancreatic juice (p. 179)
19. intestinal juice (p. 179)
20. bile (pp. 179, 180)
21. jaundice (p. 180)
22. gallstones (p. 180)
23. villi (p. 180)
24. lacteal (p. 181)
25. large intestine (p. 181)
26. appendicitis (p. 181)
27. flatus (p. 182)
28. bilirubin (p. 182)
29. artery and arteriole (p. 182)
30. capillary (p. 182)
31. venules and veins (p. 182)
32. pulmonary artery and vein (p. 184)

33. hepatic portal vein (p. 184)
34. deamination (p. 185)
35. urea (p. 185)
36. lymphatic system (p. 185)
37. edema (p. 185)
38. hemoglobin (p. 187)
39. erythrocyte (p. 187)
40. leucocyte (p. 187)
41. platelets (p. 187)
42. trachea and larynx (p. 187)
43. bronchi and bronchioles (p. 187)
44. alveoli (p. 187)
45. inspiration (p. 187)
46. expiration (p. 187)
47. nephron (p. 189)
48. filtration (p. 189)
49. tubular reabsorption (p. 189)
50. ureter (p. 191)
51. bladder (p. 191)

STUDY EXERCISES

Instructions: Write out your answers carefully and completely on a separate paper. Check your answers by referring to the text page indicated.

1. Briefly discuss how plants and animals utilize the waste products released by the other. (p. 191)
2. Describe the events that occur as a result of the ingestion and digestion of a typical meal. (pp. 175-182)
3. List the cellular components of blood. (p. 187)
4. Describe the process of filtration that occurs in the nephron. (pp. 189, 191)

SELF-POSTTEST OF LEARNING GOALS

Instructions: After completing the vocabulary in written form it is now time to review. State each definition orally several times. Reread those areas in your text associated with the study exercises on which you did poorly. Retake the pretest at this time.

ANSWERS

1. metabolism	11. pulmonary	21. a	30. d
2. stomach	12. hepatic portal	22. d	31. b
3. ileum	13. deamination	23. b	32. c
4. esophagus	14. urea	24. e	33. b
5. pyloric	15. b	25. c	34. a
6. liver	16. e	26. c	35. a
7. bilirubin	17. a	27. a	36. a, d
8. dorsal	18. d	28. c	37. a, b, c, d
9. capillaries	19. b	29. d	38. a, b
10. carotid	20. c		

Chapter 12

Transplants and Immunity

OVERVIEW

Man's ability to survive depends to a great extent on his immune capacity. We never give a second thought to the ability of bacterial or viral components to be continually inactivated or the constant production of antibodies by selected tissues. In fact, the total phenomenon of immunity is probably the least communicable among laymen. The last decade produced many different tissue transplants. Many were unsuccessful because of researchers' inability to totally supress the patient's immune response. It is important to remember that to supress the immune response of an individual, to allow a tissue transplant, reduces the patient's ability to combat foreign protein, such as bacteria and viruses. This chapter presents information about past and present research in the field of immunology, thus allowing you the opportunity to become familiar and communicable about a very important facet of your life, the immune response.

LEARNING GOALS

After successfully completing this chapter you should, orally or in writing, be able to do the following.

1. Use appropriately the vocabulary of this chapter as it relates to concepts presented.
2. Review the historical aspects of the science of immunology.
3. Discuss the results of Medawar's skin grafting experiments.
4. Describe blood cell chimerism.
5. Discuss Burnet's clonal selection theory.
6. Relate the role of the thymus to the immune response.
7. Describe the action of an immunosuppressant.

SELF-PRETEST OF LEARNING GOALS

Before proceeding further in the study of this chapter, attempt to answer the following questions without referring to other information. Upon completion of the test, compare your responses with the answer key at the end of the *Study Guide* chapter. Then correct the wrong responses by referring to the text (page numbers are indicated following each question).

Matching

1. Barnard (p. 195)
2. Jenner (pp. 195, 196)
3. Salk (p. 196)
4. Medawar (p. 197)
5. Pasteur (p. 196)
6. Burnet (p. 199)

a. discovered smallpox vaccine
b. advocated the expression *vaccination*
c. discovered polio vaccine
d. performed first heart transplant surgery
e. none of these
f. demonstrated an association between skin graft rejection and an immune response

Fill in the Blank

7. A tissue transplant from one region of the body to another region is termed an_____. (p. 199)

8. A tissue transplant between two individuals of the same species is termed an_____. (p. 199)

9. A tissue transplant between individuals of different species is termed a_____. (p. 199)

10. A group of identical cells is termed a_____. (p. 204)

11. The removal of the thymus is known as a_____. (p. 205)

VOCABULARY

These are key words you should know. By learning these you will achieve learning goal number 1. The page where the respective definition occurs is indicated following the word.

1. antigen (p. 195)
2. immune response (p. 195)
3. antibody (p. 195)
4. immunity (p. 195)
5. vaccine (p. 196)
6. autograft (p. 199)
7. allograft (p. 199)
8. heterograft (p. 199)
9. blood cell chimerism (p. 201)
10. clone (p. 204)
11. thymus (p. 205)
12. immunoglobulin (p. 207)
13. immunosuppressants (p. 208)

STUDY EXERCISES

Instructions: Write our your answers carefully and completely on a separate paper. Check your answers by referring to the text page indicated.

1. Briefly describe Medawar's experimentation concerning tissue graft rejection. (pp. 197-199)
2. Discuss how blood cell chimerism occurs. (p. 201)
3. Relate several investigations that demonstrated blood cell chimerism. (p. 201)
4. Present arguments for and/or against the concept that antibodies are genetically controlled. (pp. 203-205)

PROBE

1. If you had an organ that was not functioning properly and might cease functioning, what considerations would be foremost in your mind concerning a possible transplant?

SELF-POSTTEST OF LEARNING GOALS

Instructions: After completing the vocabulary in written form it is now time to review. State each definition orally several times. Reread those areas in your text associated with the study exercises on which you did poorly. Retake the pretest at this time.

ANSWERS

1. d	4. f	7. autograft	10. clone
2. a	5. b	8. allograft	11. thymectomy
3. c	6. e	9. heterograft	

Chapter 13

Cancer, Degenerative Diseases, and Aging

OVERVIEW

We continually strive to improve the probability of man increasing his livability. However, two major causes of death, namely, cancer and cardiovascular disease, presently inhibit any great advances in prolonging human life. All populations accept aging as a normal part of life. Major concerns are being expressed by researchers as to what controls the rate of cellular aging. Of interest to every person is how to slow down this rate. This chapter presents detailed information that relates directly to you concerning cancer, degenerative diseases, and aging.

LEARNING GOALS

After successfully completing this chapter you should be able to do the following, orally or in writing.

1. Use appropriately the vocabulary of this chapter as it relates to concepts presented.
2. Discuss the various types of cancer.
3. Briefly describe tissue changes in lung cancer.
4. Discuss the concept of repressors and regulator genes.
5. Describe the suggestion that virus particles can serve as triggering agents for malignant growth.
6. Discuss the process of arteriosclerosis.
7. Describe why diet is an important factor in controlling arteriosclerosis.
8. Relate the physiological changes that occur as a result of diabetes.
9. Describe various tissue changes that occur as a result of aging.

SELF-PRETEST OF LEARNING GOALS

Before proceeding further in the study of this chapter, attempt to answer the following questions without referring to other information. Upon completion of the test, compare your responses with the answer key at the end of the *Study Guide* chapter. Then correct the wrong responses by referring to the text (page numbers are indicated following each question).

True—False

1. Cancer-inducing agents are known as *carcinogens.* (p. 213)
   a. True   b. False

2. Hypertension is synonymous with high blood pressure. (p. 213)
   a. True   b. False

3. Arteriosclerosis is a form of cancer. (p. 213)
   a. True   b. False

4. The spread of abnormal cells to other, distant sites is termed *metastasis*. (p. 213)
   a. True   b. False

5. In all industrialized countries the incidence of cancer among males is increasing. (pp. 213, 214)
   a. True   b. False

Multiple Choice

6. Which of the following was associated with the detection of cervical cancer? (p. 214)
   a. Jamison   c. Welsh
   b. Papanicolaou   d. Williamson

7. When cancer cells exist as a localized solid mass they are called (p. 213)
   a. a tumor.   c. arteriosclerosis.
   b. leukemia.   d. none of these.

8. Which of the following types of female cancer has increased in incidence during the last decade? (p. 214)
   a. Cervical   c. Lung
   b. Uterine   d. None of these

9. Which of the following viruses cause chicken pox? (p. 216)
   a. Herpes   d. Claudine's
   b. Burkitt's   e. None of these
   c. Maynard's

10. Lung cancer typically begins in the (p. 217)
    a. lung.   c. bronchus.
    b. trachea.   d. esophagus.

11. The nucleus of a cancerous cell as compared to a normal cell has which of the following characteristics? (p. 218)
    a. Larger area   d. None of these
    b. Darker stain   e. All of these
    c. Irregular shape

12. When the walls of the alveoli (air sacs) rupture under pressure due to mucus accumulation, the condition is called (p. 218)
    a. arteriosclerosis.   c. hepatitis.
    b. emphysema.   d. diabetes.

13. Which of the following cells become permanently arrested (no cell division) after total differentiation? (pp. 218, 219)
    a. Intestine   d. Blood cells
    b. Brain   e. None of these
    c. Skin

14. Cancer-associated genes are termed (p. 220)
    a. humoral.   c. oncogene.
    b. recessive.   d. none of these.

Matching (Answers may be used more than once or not at all.)

15. Hypertension (p. 213)
16. Emphysema (p. 218)
17. Papanicolaou (p. 214)
18. Leukemia (p. 213)
19. Arteriosclerosis (p. 213)

a. respiratory system
b. cardiovascular system
c. reproductive system
d. none of these

VOCABULARY

These are key words that you should know. By learning these words you will achieve learning goal number 1. The page where the respective definition occurs is indicated following the word.

1. carcinogen (p. 213)
2. hypertension (p. 213)
3. arteriosclerosis (p. 213)
4. tumor (p. 213)
5. leukemia (p. 213)
6. metastasis (p. 213)
7. N-nitrosodimethylamine (p. 214)
8. benzopyrene (p. 214)
9. herpes virus (p. 216)

10. bronchogenic carcinoma (p. 217)
11. emphysema (p. 218)
12. repressor (p. 219)
13. regulator (p. 219)
14. cancer (pp. 213, 219)
15. leiomyoma (p. 219)
16. oncogene (p. 220)
17. gerontologist (p. 223)
18. aging (p. 223)

STUDY EXERCISES

Instructions: Write out your answers carefully and completely on a separate paper. Check your answers by referring to the text page number indicated.

1. Briefly explain how an environmental factor can induce cancer. (p. 214)
2. What tissue changes occur in lung cancer? (pp. 217, 218)
3. Briefly describe how it may be possible for virus particles to trigger carcinogenic activities. (pp. 219, 220)
4. Describe the postulate of Huebner and Todaro. (pp. 220, 221)
5. What has research shown us concerning the relationship between diet and the incidence of arteriosclerosis? (p. 222)
6. What occurs at the cellular level if a person has diabetes? (p. 222)
7. What is aging? Does heredity control aging? (pp. 223, 224)

PROBE

1. Based on the information provided at the end of chapter 13, present arguments for and against the possibility that advancements in science will allow the average adult to survive to 150 years of age.

SELF-POSTTEST OF LEARNING GOALS

Instructions: After completing the vocabulary in written form it is now time to review. State each definition orally several times. Reread those areas in your text associated with the study exercises on which you did poorly. Retake the pretest at this time.

ANSWERS

1. a	11. e
2. a	12. b
3. b	13. b
4. a	14. c
5. a	15. b
6. b	16. a
7. a	17. c
8. c	18. b
9. a	19. b
10. c	

Chapter 14

Chemical Basis of Inheritance

OVERVIEW

In just over 100 years since Gregor Mendel observed that traits are passed on from parents to offspring, man has advanced to the level that he now understands the structure and function of the DNA molecule. It is truly remarkable that the observance of the cellular regulation of protein synthesis via the DNA-RNA pathway has been accomplished. This pathway, as well as the history of experimentation in biochemical genetics, will be presented in this chapter, thus allowing you the opportunity to observe the chronology of the chemical basis of inheritance.

LEARNING GOALS

After successfully completing this chapter you should be able to do the following, orally or in writing.

1. Describe the historical chronology of the field of biochemical genetics.
2. Discuss how the research work concerning transformation changed the concept of the scientific community regarding DNA.
3. Relate the research work of Hershey and Chase, which established that DNA is the essential component of the hereditary material.
4. Draw the Watson-Crick configuration of the DNA molecule.
5. Describe the self-copying mechanism of DNA.
6. Discuss recent research that led to the isolation and synthesis of a single gene.
7. Describe how a single gene ultimately is responsible for the synthesis of a specific protein.
8. Relate how minute changes in the amino acid sequence of a protein can result in a physiological malfunction.
9. Use appropriately the vocabulary of this chapter as it relates to concepts presented.

SELF-PRETEST OF LEARNING GOALS

Before proceeding further in the study of this chapter, attempt to answer the following questions without referring to other information. Upon completion of the test, compare your responses with the answer key at the end of the *Study Guide* chapter. Then correct the wrong responses by referring to the text (page numbers are indicated following each question).

Matching

1. Mendel (p. 231)
2. Johannsen (p. 231)
3. Sutton (p. 231)
4. Morgan (p. 231)
5. Meischer (p. 232)
6. Feulgen (p. 234)
7. Avery (p. 234)
8. Hershey (pp. 236, 237)
9. Chargaff (p. 237)
10. Crick (p. 238)
11. Kornberg (p. 242)
12. Beckwith (p. 243)
13. Khorana (pp. 243, 244)

a. synthesized the first gene in the lab
b. Austrian monk who conceived modern genetics
c. worked with virulent bacteriophage
d. proposed DNA configuration
e. proposed that genes are located on chromosomes
f. coined the term *gene*
g. did extensive fruit fly chromosome studies
h. isolated first gene
i. devised, in 1924, a dye specific for DNA
j. first observed the phenomenon of transformation
k. extracted DNA from many organisms to show unity
l. first isolated DNA polymerase, an enzyme
m. designated the substance of the nucleus as *nuclein*

True—False

14. The 5-carbon sugar always found in DNA is deoxyribose. (p. 232)
    a. True   b. False

15. Adenine contains nitrogen and is classed as a purine. (p. 233)
    a. True   b. False

16. Transformation is the result of DNA being found incorporated in the ribosome. (p. 234)
    a. True   b. False

17. Viruses that attack bacterial cells are known as *bacteriophages*. (p. 236)
    a. True   b. False

18. Crick, Watson, and Wilkins received the Nobel prize in 1962 for their work on DNA configuration. (p. 238)
    a. True   b. False

19. In the structure of DNA the compound adenine is always joined to cytosine. (p. 239)
    a. True   b. False

20. Sickle-cell anemia is the result of a single amino acid being replaced in the chain of amino acids that comprise the hemoglobin molecule. (pp. 245, 246)
    a. True   b. False

VOCABULARY

These are key words that you should know. By learning these words you will achieve learning goal number 9. The page where the respective definition occurs is indicated following the word or group of words.

1. gene (pp. 231, 239, 243, 244, 246)
2. DNA (p. 232)
3. deoxyribose (p. 232)
4. nucleotide (p. 234)
5. transformation (p. 234)
6. *Escherichia coli* (pp. 236, 243)
7. bacteriophage (p. 236)
8. polypeptide (p. 244)
9. mutation (p. 246)

STUDY EXERCISES

Instructions: Write out your answers carefully and completely on a separate paper. Check your answers by referring to the text page number indicated.

1. Briefly discuss the contributions of at least five different individuals in the field of genetics since 1900. (pp. 231, 234, 236-238, 242-244)
2. Draw the structure of DNA. (pp. 238, 239)
3. Describe the phenomenon of transformation. (pp. 234, 235)
4. How is DNA able to make an exact copy of itself? (p. 239)
5. What contribution did Beckwith and his co-workers make with respect to biochemical genetics? (p. 243)
6. What is sickle-cell anemia? (pp. 245, 246)

SELF-POSTTEST OF LEARNING GOALS

Instructions: After completing the vocabulary in written form it is now time to review. State each definition orally several times. Reread those areas in your text associated with the study exercises on which you did poorly. Retake the pretest at this time.

ANSWERS

1. b	11. l
2. f	12. h
3. e	13. a
4. g	14. a
5. m	15. a
6. i	16. b
7. j	17. a
8. c	18. a
9. k	19. b
10. d	20. a

Chapter 15

Physical Basis of Inheritance

OVERVIEW

The only way a mammalian species can be maintained is through the union of male and female gametes, thereby producing a zygote which contains genetic information from each parent. Each species contains a specific number of chromosome pairs. No two animal species contain the same chromosome number. In man, for example, there are 23 pairs of chromosomes. These chromosomes are in reality aggregations of genes which in turn are aggregations of DNA molecules. Each cell nucleus contains the full complement of chromosomes. When reduction division (meiosis) occurs each egg or sperm will contain only one of each chromosome pair. Thus, each parent contributes one of each pair of chromosomes to the offspring. Then when fertilization occurs the zygote produced now contains the paired chromosomes just like each parent. Consequently, the species chromosome number has been maintained. This chapter presents material which will enable you to correlate the processes of mitosis, meiosis, and fertilization, thereby achieving a knowledge of how each species maintains itself.

LEARNING GOALS

After successfully completing this chapter you should, orally or in writing, be able to do the following.

1. Use appropriately the vocabulary associated with this chapter when discussing its concepts.
2. Describe pangenesis.
3. Discuss the process of mitosis and meiosis.
4. Explain the significance of mitosis and meiosis.
5. Compare and contrast meiosis in the human male and female.
6. Discuss how offspring have the same chromosome number as their parents.

SELF-PRETEST OF LEARNING GOALS

Before proceeding further in the study of this chapter, attempt to answer the following questions without referring to other information. Upon completion of the test, compare your responses with the answer key at the end of the *Study Guide* chapter. Then correct the wrong responses by referring to the text (page numbers are indicated following each question).

True—False

1. The theory of pangenesis was developed by Charles Darwin. (p. 249)
   a. True   b. False

2. Egg and sperm are referred to as *germ cells.* (p. 249)
   a. True   b. False

3. The theory of pangenesis stated that all organs of the body contribute to the sperm and egg in the form of small particles. (p. 249)
   a. True   b. False

4. Chromosomes occur in pairs in the sperm and egg. (p. 251)
   a. True   b. False

5. Man has 46 pairs of chromosomes in the nucleus of every body cell. (p. 250)
   a. True   b. False

Matching

6. Flemming (p. 250)   a. designed pangenesis
7. Darwin (p. 249)   b. coined the term *mitosis*
8. Castle (p. 249)   c. successfully refuted pangenesis through ovarian
                                  grafts

Matching

 9. Interphase (p. 251)   a. chromosomes first become evident
10. Prophase (p. 251)   b. resting stage
11. Metaphase (p. 253)   c. chromosomes collect in center of spindle
12. Anaphase (p. 253)   d. chromosomes move to opposite poles of cell

Fill in the Blank

13. In early mitosis each chromatid remains joined together only at a small region, termed the
    _____. (p. 253)

14. A term synonymous with *haploid* is _____. (p. 251)

15. Reduction division is also termed_____. (p. 251)

16. Cells possessing paired chromosomes are said to be_____. (p. 251)

17. The number of chromosomes in each human egg or sperm is_____. (p. 251)

18. _____is the process whereby two daughter cells receive identical copies of the chromosome complement of the parent cell. (p. 253)

19. Two identical chromosomes are termed_____. (p. 256)

20. Mitosis is characterized by one division, whereas meiosis involves_____separate divisions. (p. 258)

21. The overall outcome of meiosis is the formation of_____haploid cells from a single diploid cell. (p. 258)

22. The germinal cells of the human testes are termed_____. (p. 258)

Matching (Answers may be used more than once or not at all.)

23. Spermatogonia (p. 258)   a. haploid—male
24. Spermatozoa (p. 258)   b. diploid—male
25. Muscle cell (pp. 250, 251)   c. haploid—female
26. Ovum (p. 258)   d. diploid—female
27. Liver cell (p. 251)   e. diploid—both sexes
28. Uterus cell (p. 251)
29. Oocyte (p. 258)
30. Brain cell (p. 251)

VOCABULARY

These are key words you should know. By learning these words you will achieve learning goal number 1. The page where the respective definition occurs is indicated following the word.

1. pangenesis (p. 249)
2. chromosomes (p. 249)
3. mitosis (p. 250)
4. meiosis (p. 251)
5. diploid (p. 251)
6. haploid (p. 251)
7. interphase (p. 251)
8. prophase (p. 251)
9. chromatid (p. 253)
10. centromere (p. 253)
11. centriole (p. 253)

12. metaphase (p. 253)
13. anaphase (p. 253)
14. telophase (p. 253)
15. homologues (p. 256)
16. synapsis (p. 256)
17. tetrad (p. 257)
18. dyad (p. 258)
19. spermatogonia (p. 258)
20. oocyte (p. 258)
21. ovum (p. 258)
22. polar body (p. 258, 260)

STUDY EXERCISES

Instructions: Write out your answers carefully and completely on a separate paper. Check your answers by referring to the text page number indicated.

1. Briefly describe the stages of mitosis. (pp. 251, 253)
2. Discuss how a single ovum contains a haploid number of chromosomes. (pp. 258-260)
3. What is the significance of meiosis and mitosis? (pp. 251, 253, 254, 260, 261)

SELF-POSTTEST OF LEARNING GOALS

Instructions: After completing the vocabulary in written form it is now time to review. State each definition orally several times. Reread those areas in your text associated with the study exercises on which you did poorly. Retake the pretest at this time.

ANSWERS

1. a
2. a
3. a
4. b
5. b
6. b
7. a
8. c
9. b
10. a
11. c
12. d
13. centromere
14. monoploid
15. meiosis

16. diploid
17. 23
18. Mitosis
19. homologues
20. two
21. four
22. spermatogonia
23. b
24. a
25. e
26. c
27. e
28. d
29. d
30. e

Chapter 16

Mendel's Work and the Principles of Inheritance

OVERVIEW

Many scientific achievements are the result of extensive spending of money following numerous hours of research group planning. One major advance in science came as the result of careful planning by one man (Mendel), a small plot of ground (20' x 120') at a monastery and some seeds (of the pea plant). As a result of these carefully controlled experiments utilizing the common pea plant, Mendel was to demonstrate and record many of the modern laws of genetics. His brilliant work lay ignored and unappreciated for over three decades after his work was published. This chapter presents in great detail the work of this Austrian monk and relates his findings to later research in the field of genetics.

LEARNING GOALS

After successfully completing this chapter you should, orally or in writing, be able to do the following.

1. Use appropriately the vocabulary associated with this chapter when discussing its concepts.
2. Discuss the chronology of rejection and acceptance of Mendel's research.
3. Describe the law of segregation, the law of independent assortment, and the principle of linkage.
4. Discuss the phenomenon of crossing over.

SELF-PRETEST OF LEARNING GOALS

Before proceeding further in the study of this chapter, attempt to answer the following questions without referring to other information. Upon completion of the test, compare your responses with the answer key at the end of the *Study Guide* chapter. Then correct the wrong responses by referring to the text (page numbers are indicated following each question).

Multiple Choice

1. Which type of plant did Mendel use for his genetic experiments? (p. 265)
   - a. Pea
   - b. Bean
   - c. Carrot
   - d. Carnation
   - e. None of these

2. What was the approximate date when Mendel's results were published? (p. 265)
   - a. 1660
   - b. 1700
   - c. 1870
   - d. 1925
   - e. 1580
   - f. 1900

3. What was the approximate date when Mendel's genetic laws were fully appreciated and the science of heredity is recorded as having been born? (p. 265)
   - a. 1660
   - b. 1900
   - c. 1700
   - d. 1925
   - e. 1580
   - f. 1870

Fill in the Blank

4. In a simple genetic cross the trait that presents itself in the F_1 generation is said to be _____. (p. 269)

5. Mendel's factors of heredity are now known as_____. (p. 269)

6. If a gene pair is symbolized as *Tt* the unlike condition is termed_____. (p. 269)

7. If a gene pair is symbolized as *TT* the like condition is termed_____. (p. 269)

8. Mendel's first law, which states that only one member of any pair of genes in a parent is transmitted to each offspring, is known as the law of_____. (p. 269)

9. If tall is dominant over short and a homozygous tall plant is crossed with a short plant, how many of 10 offspring would you expect to be tall?_____ (pp. 268, 270)

10. If tall is dominant over short and an individual exhibits a genotype of *Tt,* what is this individual's phenotype?_____(p. 270)

True—False

11. The specific site a gene occupies on the chromosome is termed the *locus.* (p. 270)
    a. True   b. False

12. The alternate gene of the gene pair is termed an *allele.* (p. 270)
    a. True   b. False

13. Mendel's law of independent assortment states that each trait (one gene pair) is associated with another trait or gene pair on the same chromosome. (p. 272)
    a. True   b. False

14. The genotype *TTyy* is said to be heterozygous. (p. 269)
    a. True   b. False

15. If tall *(T)* is dominant over short *(t)* and two heterozygous individuals are crossed, the phenotypic ratio will be 3 tall : 1 short. (p. 270)
    a. True   b. False

16. Gametes contain only one chromosome of each chromosome pair. (p. 270)
    a. True   b. False

17. The number of possible gametes from an individual with the genotype *AaBB* is four. (pp. 270, 271)
    a. True   b. False

18. Genes located together in any one chromosome are said to be *linked.* (p. 277)
    a. True   b. False

19. The principle of linkage is one of the major laws of inheritance. (p. 277)
    a. True   b. False

20. Should homologous chromosomes exchange genes during meiosis the phenomenon is termed crossing over. (p. 277)
    a. True   b. False

21. Crossing over decreases variability. (p. 278)
    a. True   b. False

VOCABULARY

These are key words you should know. By learning these words you will achieve learning goal number 1. The page where the respective definition occurs is indicated following the word.

1. dominant (p. 269)
2. recessive (p. 269)
3. homozygous (p. 269)
4. heterozygous (p. 269)
5. Mendel's law (pp. 269, 272)
6. phenotype (p. 270)

7. genotype (p. 270)
8. locus (p. 270)
9. allele (p. 270)
10. phenotypic ratio (pp. 270, 273)
11. crossing over (p. 277)

STUDY EXERCISES

Instructions: Write out your answers carefully and completely on a separate paper. Check your answers by referring to the text page number indicated.

1. Briefly describe how Mendel's contribution was rediscovered. (pp. 265, 266)
2. State each of Mendel's genetic laws. (pp. 269, 272)
3. Describe how crossing over may occur. (pp. 277-280)

PROBLEM SOLVING

General Information

All gametes are produced through the process of meiosis. When two gametes join in fertilization, a zygote is produced. All gametes are haploid, whereas all zygotes are diploid.

The basis for genetics lies in the fact that for every trait there is a gene with a specific DNA sequence and a partner associated with the same trait located on the adjacent chromosome pair. Remember, all diploid ($2n$) cells have every chromosome occuring in pairs. The only haploid (n) cells are the gametes produced through meiosis (egg and sperm). Likewise, the number of pairs of chromosomes is species specific. For man (*Homo sapiens sapiens*) there are 23 pairs, 46 total chromosomes. All human cells (except the sperm and egg) contain 23 pairs.

When a gene is capable of expressing itself in either the homozygous dominant or heterozygous state, the trait is said to be *completely dominant*.

Example: Trait is tallness of corn.

Gene T = dominant
Gene t = recessive

$\left.\begin{array}{c} TT \\ Tt \end{array}\right\}$ Tall

tt – Short

TT = Homozygous dominant
Tt = Heterozygous
tt = Homozygous recessive

When the heterozygote does not appear (phenotype) as either the homozygous dominant or homozygous recessive, the trait is said to be *incompletely dominant*.

Example: Trait is color of petals in carnations.

Genes: R RR = Red
          r Rr = Pink
                    rr = White

In any genetic problem you will always be given whether the trait exists as complete or incomplete dominance.

Specific Problems

1. MONOHYBRID CROSS: genetic cross involving only *one* trait.

   a. *Example:* Trait is coat color. There is complete dominance (brown is dominant over white). If a heterozygous male and a heterozygous female have sexual relations, what is the number of brown-coated offspring you would expect in a litter of four offspring?

   Solution: Let B gene be dominate δBb x $\female Bb$ — genotypes of parents
   b gene be recessive

	$\female B$	b
δ B	BB	Bb
b	Bb	bb

   BB — brown   Thus: 3/4 would be brown-coated
   Bb — brown
   bb — white

   We observe that the genotypic ratio is 1:2:1.

   We observe that the phenotypic ratio is 3:1.

   Remember that the genotype is the actual DNA arrangement of the gene in the nucleus, whereas the phenotype is what you can see by looking at the plant or animal (color, height, etc.).

   b. *Example:* Trait is petal color in carnations. There is incomplete dominance (red-pink-white).

   (1) How many pink carnations out of 1,000 would you expect if you crossed the pollen of a red with the eggs of a white?

   (2) Out of 1,000 how many pink would you expect if you crossed two pink plants?

   (3) What would be the phenotypic ratio in b (above problem)?

   Solution A: RR = red δRR x $rr \female$ = Rr 1,000 of 1,000 pink
   Rr = pink
   rr = white

   Solution A: δRr x $Rr \female$

	$\female R$	r
δ R	RR	Rr
r	Rr	rr

   $\dfrac{2}{4}$ x $\dfrac{1,000}{1}$ = 500 pink

   Solution A: red (RR) 1
   pink (Rr) 2   1:2:1 ratio
   white (rr) 1

   ---

2. DIHYBRID CROSS: genetic cross involving *two* traits, which may or may not be one and the same chromosome. Each trait will be given as being complete or incomplete with respect to dominance.

Nucleus of cell   Nucleus of cell

What we are doing is observing the action of two pairs of genes at the same time.

a. *Example:* The trait for tallness-shortness is completely dominant. The trait for eye color (brown-blue) is completely dominant. If both male (♂) and female (♀) are heterozygous for both traits, how many of 100 will be brown-eyed and tall?

Solution: ♂*TtBb* x ♀*TtBb*

	♀ *TB*	*Tb*	*tB*	*tb*
TB	*TTBB*	*TTBb*	*TtBB*	*TtBb*
Tb	*TTBb*	*TTbb*	*TtBb*	*Ttbb*
tB	*TtBB*	*TtBb*	*ttBB*	*ttBb*
tb	*TtBb*	*Ttbb*	*ttBb*	*ttbb*

♂ (label for left side)

$$\frac{9}{16} \times \frac{100}{1} = 56.25$$

tall/brown — 9
tall/blue — 3
short/brown — 3
short/blue — 1
—
16

3. SEX-LINKED TRAITS: one pair of chromosomes determines the sex (XX=female; XY=male). If a trait has its gene pair associated with the sex chromosomes, then the trait is said to be sex-linked. Note below that the Y chromosome is structurally shorter than the X chromosome.

X   Y

Male

X   X

Female

Notice that in the male there is no gene on the bottom of the Y chromosome; thus the trait expresses itself through only a single gene, not a gene pair.

a. *Example:* The trait for baldness is sex-linked. It is completely dominant. If a *bald-headed male* has sexual relations with a *normal-haired female,* how many of 10 offspring would you expect to be normal-haired males?

B = baldness
b = normal

$X^B Y$ (x) $X^b X^b$

	X^b
X^B	$X^B X^b$
Y	$X^b Y$

Note that all male offspring will be normal-haired and

XY = male XX = female
So: 1/2 are males
So: 5 of 10 will be normal-haired males

Example Problems

    a.   MONOHYBRID CROSS

        1. In summer squash, white fruit color dominates over yellow. A white-fruited squash plant when crossed with a yellow-fruited one produced 87 white and 85 yellow-fruited plants.

What are the genotypes of the parents?_____

If the white-fruited parent is self-fertilized, what will be the fruit color of the offspring?

_____

        2. In tomatoes, the skin may be smooth or hairy. Crosses between a smooth-skinned and a hairy-skinned tomato gave 607 smooth fruits. Two of these F_1 plants were crossed and produced 201 hairy-skinned fruits and 609 smooth-skinned fruits.

Which character is dominant and which is recessive?_____

_____

        3. In fruit flies eye color is *sex-linked,* that is, genes for eye color are carried only on the X sex chromosomes. In males, the pair of sex chromosomes is designated XY, while in the female the pair is designated XX. Thus, in males genes for eye color are carried on only the one X chromosome. Red eye color is dominant over the recessive white eye color. Cross a white-eyed male and a homozygous red-eyed female; work out the F_1 generation.

    b.   DIHYBRID CROSS—Tall dominant over short; green dominant over white.

        1. Cross a tall, green corn plant (*TtGG*) with a dwarf white corn plant (*ttgg*).

What kind of gametes will be produced by each parent?_____

What is the phenotype of the F_1?_____

What phenotypes would be produced and in what ratio if two heterozygous F_1s were crossed?_____

_____

Of 960 offspring, how many would be tall and green?_____

Solutions to Example Problems

You may use any symbols you wish to solve a genetics problem.

1. Monohybrid Cross
   a. Summer Squash
      (1) Let W = dominant white; w = recessive yellow
      (2) What genotypes could produce white phenotypes?
          Answer: WW and Ww
      (3) What genotype could produce a yellow phenotype?
          Answer: ww
      (4) What gametes would be produced by a heterozygous white *(ww)*?
          Answer: W and w
      (5) What gamete would be produced by a yellow squash?
          Answer: w
      (6) Observe the problem states that a white x yellow produced 87 white and 85 yellow. This represents a 1:1 phenotypic ratio. In a ratio, numbers seldom will be exact, but approximate. Thus, 87:85 is approximately a 1:1 ratio.
      (7) Remember, we were crossing white x yellow.

Ww x ww

Gametes W, w *(w)*

	w
W	Ww
w	ww

Ww — White
ww — Yellow

Thus, the genotypes of the parents are Ww and ww.

      (8) Now, if the white-fruited parent is self-fertilized, we have:

Ww x Ww Gametes W,w *(W, w)* W,w

	W	w
W	WW	Ww
w	Ww	ww

So: WW = White — 1 of 4
    Ww = White — 2 of 4
    ww = Yellow — 1 of 4

Thus, 3 of 4 would be white; 1 of 4 would be yellow.

The phenotypic ratio is 3 white: 1 yellow.

The genotypic ratio is 1 *(WW)*:2*(Ww)*:1*(ww)*.

   b. Tomato Skin Texture
      (1) You must figure out which trait is dominant.
      (2) You are told that the traits are smooth skin and hairy skin and that a smooth x hairy cross gave all (607) smooth fruits.
      (3) When two F_1 (first generation) individuals are crossed you observe a 3 (smooth):1(hairy) ratio. Remember, numbers are approximate; 609:201 is approximately a 3:1 ratio.

(4) Let S = smooth; s = hairy

If $SS \times ss$ occurs, the gametes are S s;
thus Ss is the genotype for all offspring and the F_1 cross of $Ss \times Ss$ produces

	S	s
S	SS	Ss
s	Ss	ss

So: SS = smooth − 1 of 4
Ss = smooth − 2 of 4
ss = hairy − 1 of 4

Therefore, smooth is dominant over hairy.

c. Fruit Flies
(1) This is a sex-linked problem.
(2) Trait is carried on only the X chromosome.
(3) Red eye color is dominant over white eye color.
(4) The cross given:
White-eyed male and red-eyed (homozygous) female
Thus: R = red, r = white
male is _r, female is RR

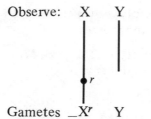 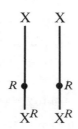

So, the male can produce two sperm types.

One is (X^r), the other is (Y). All eggs are X^R.

Thus:

	X^R
X^r	$X^R X^r$
Y	$X^R Y$

So: $X^R X^r$ − female (XX) red-eyed
$X^R Y$ − male (XY) red-eyed

2. Dihybrid Cross
   a. Two traits are observed.
   b. Both traits are completely dominant.
   c. Cross is: $TtGG \times ttgg$
      gametes: TG, tG (tg)
   d. Each gamete (sperm or egg) contains one gene for each trait (height and color).

e.

	tg
TG	TtGg
tG	ttGg

So: Phenotypic ratio is 1 (tall-green) : 1 (short-green)

f. Two heterozygous F_1 are crossed: *TtGg* x *TtGg*
    gametes: *TG, Tg, tG, tg, TG, Tg, tG, tg*

	TG	Tg	tG	tg
TG	TTGG	TTGg	TtGG	TtGg
Tg	TTGg	TTgg	TtGg	Ttgg
tG	TtGG	TtGg	ttGG	ttGg
tg	TtGg	Ttgg	ttGg	ttgg

$$
\left.\begin{array}{l} TTGG - 1 \\ TTGg - 2 \\ TtGG - 2 \\ TtGg - 4 \end{array}\right\}
$$
These are genotypes that produce tall-green individuals.

$$
\left.\begin{array}{l} TTgg - 1 \\ Ttgg - 2 \end{array}\right\}
$$
These are genotypes that produce tall-white individuals.

$$
\left.\begin{array}{l} ttGG - 1 \\ ttGg - 2 \end{array}\right\}
$$
These are genotypes that produce dwarf-green individuals.

$$
\left.\begin{array}{l} ttgg - 1 \\ 16 \end{array}\right\}
$$
This genotype is dwarf and white.

Thus, 9 of 16 will be tall and green.

So: $\dfrac{9}{16} \times \dfrac{960}{1} = 540$ of 960 will be tall and green.

The phenotypic ratio is 9 (tall-green):3 (tall-white):3 (dwarf-green):1 (dwarf- white)

SELF-POSTTEST OF LEARNING GOALS

Instructions: After completing the vocabulary in written form it is now time to review. State each definition orally several times. Reread those areas in your text associated with the study exercises on which you did poorly. Retake the pretest at this time.

ANSWERS

1. a
2. c
3. b
4. dominant
5. genes
6. heterozygous
7. homozygous
8. segregation
9. 10
10. tall
11. a
12. a
13. b
14. b
15. a
16. a
17. b
18. a
19. a
20. a
21. b

Chapter 17

Mendelian Inheritance in Man

OVERVIEW

Universally, organisms that produce large numbers of offspring in a relatively short span of time are used by geneticists to study inheritance. Man does not meet either of these qualifications. Thus the data on human inheritance must be accumulated by specifically analyzing large numbers of human pedigrees. This chapter presents material that will allow you to better understand your own inheritance and how you received genetic information from your parents.

LEARNING GOALS

After successfully completing this chapter you should, orally or in writing, be able to do the following.

1. Use appropriately the vocabulary associated with this chapter when discussing its concepts.
2. Draw the symbols for male and female as used by geneticists.
3. Describe several recessively inherited human disorders.
4. Discuss lethal recessive genes.
5. Describe disorders associated with dominant inheritance.
6. Discuss genes that are not active until late in life.
7. Describe why there are few homozygous dominant lethal traits.

SELF-PRETEST OF LEARNING GOALS

Before proceeding further in the study of this chapter, attempt to answer the following questions without referring to other information. Upon completion of the test, compare your responses with the answer key at the end of the *Study Guide* chapter. Then correct the wrong responses by referring to the text (page numbers are indicated following each question).

Matching

1. Pycnodysostosis (p. 288)   a. recessive disorder (nonlethal)
2. Cystic fibrosis (p. 292)   b. recessive, lethal

Matching

3. Albinism (p. 283)   a. recessive disorder (nonlethal)
4. Huntington's chorea (p. 296) b. recessive, lethal
5. Marfan's syndrome (p. 293)   c. dominant disorder
6. Phenylketonuria (p. 288)   d. none of these
7. Tay-Sachs disease (pp. 291, 292)
8. Achondroplasia (p. 293)
9. Anonychia (p. 293)
10. Anophthalmia (p. 287)

True—False

11. The simplest inheritance pattern is one in which the trait is governed by a single pair of genes. (p. 283)
    a. True   b. False

12. The genetic symbol for the male is ♂. (p. 285)
    a. True   b. False

13. Marriages involving close relatives are termed *consanguineous.* (p. 286)
    a. True   b. False

14. Children are genetically referred to as *siblings.* (p. 286)
    a. True   b. False

15. Few lethal dominant genes have been observed. (p. 296)
    a. True   b. False

VOCABULARY

These are key words or phrases that you should know. By learning these you will achieve learning goal number 1. The page where the respective definition occurs is indicated following the word or phrase.

1. albinism (p. 283)
2. propositus (p. 286)
3. proposita (p. 286)
4. anophthalmia (p. 287)
5. pycnodysostosis (p. 288)
6. phenylketonuria (p. 288)
7. Tay-Sachs disease (p. 292)
8. cystic fibrosis (p. 292)
9. tylosis (p. 293)
10. anonychia (p. 293)
11. brachydactyly (p. 293)
12. polydactyly (p. 293)
13. Marfan's syndrome (p. 293)
14. Huntington's chorea (p. 296)
15. consanguineous (p. 286)

STUDY EXERCISES

Instructions: Write out your answers carefully and completely on a separate paper. Check your answers by referring to the text page number indicated.

1. What is a lethal recessive gene? (pp. 291, 292)
2. Briefly describe cystic fibrosis. (p. 292)
3. Why are there so few homozygous dominant lethal traits? (p. 296)

PROBE

1. Do you think science should pursue the possibility of being able to identify gene types in adults prior to parenthood? Likewise, should prospective parents be told of possible gene combinations that would result in deformities or that would be lethal?

SELF-POSTTEST OF LEARNING GOALS

Instructions: After completing the vocabulary in written form it is now time to review. State each definition orally several times. Reread those areas in your text associated with the study exercises on which you did poorly. Retake the pretest at this time.

ANSWERS

1. a
2. b
3. a
4. c
5. c
6. a
7. b
8. c

9. c
10. a
11. a
12. a
13. a
14. a
15. a

Chapter 18

Man's Hemoglobins and Gene Action

OVERVIEW

The function of a gene is to direct the synthesis of a specific protein. This is accomplished via the DNA-RNA message system. All proteins are nothing more than a specific arrangement of selected amino acids. The difference between humans is expressed physically through variations in the number and sequence of the amino acids in the many proteins that are a part of every cell. This chapter presents a detailed study of a selected protein, hemoglobin, which was initially utilized to prove the existence of a gene-protein relationship.

LEARNING GOALS

After successfully completing this chapter you should, orally or in writing, be able to do the following.

1. Use appropriately the vocabulary associated with this chapter when discussing its concepts.
2. State the function of hemoglobin.
3. Describe the genetic abnormality, sickle-cell anemia.
4. Discuss how the sickle-cell hemoglobin molecule is altered by an errant gene.
5. State the component difference between DNA and RNA.
6. Explain the role of a codon in protein synthesis.
7. Describe the process of genetic transcription.
8. Discuss the transfer of information from messenger RNA to protein via translation.
9. Explain how a genetic mutation may occur.

SELF-PRETEST OF LEARNING GOALS

Before proceeding further in the study of this chapter, attempt to answer the following questions without referring to other information. Upon completion of the test, compare your responses with the answer key at the end of the *Study Guide* chapter. Then correct the wrong responses by referring to the text (page numbers are indicated following each question).

True—False

1. The properties of any protein are determined by the number, identity, and arrangement of the amino acids. (p. 301)
   a. True   b. False

2. Hemoglobin is a main component of white blood cells and transports oxygen to all parts of the animal body. (p. 301)
   a. True   b. False

3. Sickle-cell anemia occurs predominantly in Negroes. (p. 302)
   a. True   b. False

4. The sickle-cell anemic patient inherits two defective genes from each parent. (p. 302)
   a. True   b. False

5. Linus Pauling discovered that the defective sickling gene alters the configuration of the hemo-globin molecule. (p. 304)
   a. True   b. False

6. The difference between the chemical composition of normal and sickle-cell hemoglobin is the arrangement of just three amino acids. (p. 305)
   a. True   b. False

7. The DNA bases can exist in several rare alternative forms known as *tautomers.* (p. 307)
   a. True   b. False

Multiple Choice

8. Which of the following is found in DNA but not in RNA? (p. 307)
   a. Ribose   d. Adenine
   b. Uracil   e. Guanine
   c. Thymine

9. Which of the following is found in RNA but not in DNA? (p. 307)
   a. Ribose   d. Adenine
   b. Urea   e. Guanine
   c. Thymine

10. Each three-letter unit of the messenger RNA is called a (p. 309)
   a. codon.   d. lysine.
   b. allele.   e. flog.
   c. gamete.

11. Who was responsible for demonstrating which codon signifies which amino acid? (p. 309)
   a. Lansteiner   c. Nirenberg
   b. Harvey   d. Pauling

12. The transfer of information from DNA to messenger RNA has been called (p. 310)
   a. transcription.   c. configuration.
   b. allele.   d. transamination.

13. The transfer of information from messenger RNA to proteins is termed (p. 310)
   a. transcription.   c. configuration.
   b. translation.   d. allele.

14. In sickle-cell anemia the amino acid, glutamic acid, is replaced by another amino acid known as (pp. 305, 312)
   a. glycine.   d. methionine.
   b. valine.   e. tryptophan.
   c. arginine.

15. Normal hemoglobin (HbA) contains how many polypeptide chains? (p. 313)
   a. 4   d. 7
   b. 6   e. 2
   c. 8

Fill in the Blank

16. _____ is the smallest number of DNA bases independently capable of producing a mutant phenotype. (p. 316)

17. A given gene can exist in several forms. This is referred to as _____ allelism. (p. 316)

VOCABULARY

These are key words or phrases that you should know. By learning these you will achieve learning goal number 1. The page where the respective definition occurs is indicated following the word or phrase.

1. gene (p. 301)
2. hemoglobin (p. 301)
3. sickle-cell anemia (pp. 301, 302)
4. glutamic acid (p. 305)
5. valine (p. 305)
6. tautomer (p. 307)
7. RNA (p. 307)
8. mRNA (p. 308)
9. codon (p. 309)
10. transcription (p. 310)
11. translation (p. 310)
12. ribosomal RNA (p. 310)
13. anticodon (p. 310)
14. hemoglobin C (p. 312)
15. multiple alleles (pp. 313, 316)
16. hemoglobin A (pp. 304, 314)
17. cistron (p. 316)
18. muton (p. 316)

STUDY EXERCISES

Instructions: Write out your answers carefully and completely on a separate paper. Check your answers by referring to the text page number indicated.

1. Briefly describe the structural difference between hemoglobin A and hemoglobin S. (pp. 304, 305)
2. How does RNA differ from DNA? (pp. 307, 308)
3. Describe the role of the codon as it relates to messenger RNA. (pp. 309, 310)
4. Explain how a genetic mutation may occur. (p. 316)

SELF-POSTTEST OF LEARNING GOALS

Instructions: After completing the vocabulary in written form it is now time to review. State each definition orally several times. Reread those areas in your text associated with the study exercises on which you did poorly. Retake the pretest at this time.

ANSWERS

1. a
2. b
3. a
4. b
5. a
6. b
7. a
8. c
9. a
10. a
11. c
12. a
13. b
14. b
15. a
16. Muton
17. multiple

Chapter 19

Human Blood Groups and Hemolytic Disease

OVERVIEW

Many times in an animal species two genes or alleles may control the production of two separate proteins, with each protein contributing to a single physiological event. This condition of multiple alleles is very evident in the inheritance of human blood groups. This basic mechanism of inheritance was initially proposed in the first part of this century. This chapter will explain to you the human ABO blood groups and the inheritance of various hemolytic diseases.

LEARNING GOALS

After successfully completing this chapter you should, orally or in writing, be able to do the following.

1. Describe the research that led to our present understanding of blood cell antigens.
2. Use appropriately the vocabulary associated with this chapter when discussing its concepts.
3. Explain the genetic difference between persons with A, O, B, or AB blood types.
4. Describe ABO and Rh incompatibility.
5. Discuss how an immunosuppressant was developed to aid in the control of Rh disease.

SELF-PRETEST OF LEARNING GOALS

Before proceeding further in the study of this chapter, attempt to answer the following questions without referring to other information. Upon completion of the test, compare your responses with the answer key at the end of the *Study Guide* chapter. Then correct the wrong responses by referring to the text (page numbers are indicated following each question).

Matching

1. Landsteiner (p. 319)
2. Smith (pp. 329, 330)
3. Levine (p. 325)
4. Freda (pp. 329, 330)

a. postulated relationship between Rh factor and hemolytic disease
b. passive immunity can prevent active immunity
c. developed an immunosuppressant
d. discovered red blood cell agglutination

True–False

5. An antigen is a protein. (p. 319)
   a. True   b. False

6. In hemolytic disease of the newborn, the hemoglobin liberated from the ruptured cells is transformed into bilirubin. (p. 324)
   a. True   b. False

7. Erythroblastosis fetalis occurs only in female babies. (p. 328)
   a. True   b. False

Multiple Choice

8. Which of the following is *not* a human blood group? (p. 320)
   a. A
   b. B
   c. C
   d. O

9. Where are fetal Rh antigens produced? (p. 326)
   a. Red blood cell
   b. Thyroid
   c. Lung
   d. Liver

10. Which of the following groups have the greatest frequency of Rh negative individuals? (p. 328)
   a. Caucasians
   b. American Indians
   c. African Negroes
   d. Japanese

11. What type of molecule was the immunosuppressant developed by Freda, Gorman, and Pollack to suppress the production of antibodies in Rh negative mothers? (p. 330)
   a. Gamma globulin
   b. Valine
   c. Testosterone
   d. Estrone

VOCABULARY

These are key words or phrases that you should know. By learning these you will achieve learning goal number 2. The page where the respective definition occurs is indicated following the word or phrase.

1. agglutinate (p. 319)
2. antigen (p. 319)
3. antibody (p. 319)
4. ABO blood groups (p. 320)
5. bilirubin (p. 324)
6. erythroblastosis fetalis (p. 328)

STUDY EXERCISES

Instructions: Write out your answers carefully and completely on a separate paper. Check your answers by referring to the text page number indicated.

1. What is the difference between a person with type O blood and one with type A blood? (pp. 321, 323, 324)
2. Can blood-group tests, in the case of disputed parentage, prove that a certain man is definitely the father of a specific child? (p. 323)
3. Describe how an immunosuppressant was developed for the control of Rh disease. (pp. 329, 330)

SELF-POSTTEST OF LEARNING GOALS

Instructions: After completing the vocabulary in written form it is now time to review. State each definition orally several times. Reread those areas in your text associated with the study exercises on which you did poorly. Retake the pretest at this time.

ANSWERS

1. d
2. b
3. a
4. c
5. a
6. a
7. b
8. c
9. a
10. a
11. a

Chapter 20

Inborn Errors of Metabolism

OVERVIEW

Proteins are either utilized as a functional unit for a given period of time or inactivated rapidly when they function as an enzyme. Enzymes are subject to intracellular modifications, as are structural proteins such as hemoglobin. Remember that all enzymes are protein, but all proteins are not enzymes. The modification of any protein occurs because of amino acid substitution in the polypeptide change or the rate of synthesis of the complete polypeptide chain. Many of the inborn errors of metabolism are due to some change in the polypeptide chain, thus producing an enzyme deficiency. This chapter presents the historical aspects of inborn errors as well as specifically describing many inherited biochemical anomalies of man.

LEARNING GOALS

After successfully completing this chapter you should, orally or in writing, be able to do the following.

1. Describe past research that has led to our current knowledge of certain inborn errors of metabolism.
2. Use appropriately the vocabulary associated with this chapter when discussing its concepts.
3. Discuss the consequences of the alteration of a single enzyme.
4. Describe, specifically, phenylketonuria and several phenylalanine deficiencies.
5. Explain how galactosemia occurs.

SELF-PRETEST OF LEARNING GOALS

Before proceeding further in the study of this chapter, attempt to answer the following questions without referring to other information. Upon completion of the test, compare your responses with the answer key at the end of the *Study Guide* chapter. Then correct the wrong responses by referring to the text (page numbers are indicated following each question).

Matching

1. Garrod (p. 333)
2. Beadle (p. 334)
3. Fölling (p. 335)
4. Jervis (p. 337)
5. Guthrie (p. 339)

    a. one gene-one enzyme concept
    b. described alkaptonuria
    c. described first case of PKU
    d. devised test to detect abnormal phenylalanine levels
    e. found PKU infants are deficient in a liver enzyme

Multiple Choice

6. In albinism the body is incapable of synthesizing (p. 341)
    a. tyrosine.
    b. melanin.
    c. phenylalanine.
    d. galactose.

7. In galactosemia infants are unable to use (p. 341)
   a.   glucose.
   b.   galactose.
   c.   phenylalanine.
   d.   sucrose.

Matching

 8. Tyrosinosis (p. 341)
 9. Albinism (p. 341)
10. PKU (p. 336)
11. Hunter's syndrome (p. 343)
12. von Gierke's disease (p. 344)

a.   phenylalanine
b.   mucopolysaccharide
c.   tyrosine
d.   glucose-6-phosphate
e.   melanin

True—False

13. Alkaptonuria is a genetically recessive condition. (p. 333)
    a.   True
    b.   False

14. Beadle and Tatum set forth the one gene-one enzyme concept. (p. 334)
    a.   True
    b.   False

15. Metachromasia is synonymous with "change in color." (p. 343)
    a.   True
    b.   False

VOCABULARY

These are key words that you should know. By learning these you will achieve learning goal number 2. The page where the respective definition occurs is indicated following the word.

1. alkaptonuria (p. 333)
2. neurospora (p. 334)
3. phenylketonuria (pp. 335-340)
4. tyrosine (p. 337)
5. tyrosinosis (p. 341)

 6. albinism (p. 341)
 7. galactosemia (p. 341)
 8. metachromasia (p. 343)
 9. von Gierke's disease (p. 344)
10. melanin (p. 341)

STUDY EXERCISES

Instructions: Write out your answers carefully and completely on a separate paper. Check your answers by referring to the text page indicated.

1. What causes phenylketonuria? (p. 337)
2. Briefly describe the symptoms of galactosemia. (p. 341)
3. What are the essential principles underlying treatment of inherited metabolic disorders? (p. 346)

PROBE

1. Based on materials presented in this chapter, present arguments for or against the possibility of actually replacing defective genes in human cells within the next 25 years.

SELF-POSTTEST OF LEARNING GOALS

Instructions: After completing the vocabulary and study exercises in written form it is now time to review. State each definition orally several times. Reread those areas in your text associated with the study exercises on which you did poorly. Retake the pretest at this time.

ANSWERS

1. b
2. a
3. c
4. e
5. d
6. b
7. b
8. c

9. e
10. a
11. b
12. d
13. a
14. a
15. a

Chapter 21

Regulation of Gene Action

OVERVIEW

Each cell in the human body, except sperm and egg, contain the same 23 pairs of chromosomes. Why then do not all cells function in a similar manner? The answer lies in the fact that each specialized cell produces only selected proteins. Since a protein is produced under the influence of a specific gene, through the DNA-RNA-ribosome pathway, it is evident that gene action varies from cell to cell. That is, all cells have the genetic capacity to produce insulin, yet only the pancreas does so. Each cell synthesizes only the protein that relates to that cell's needs. This chapter presents material concerning gene action that will allow you to understand how certain genes are active only in selected cells.

LEARNING GOALS

After successfully completing this chapter you should, orally or in writing, be able to do the following.

1. Describe the operon hypothesis as stated by Jocab and Monod.
2. Discuss the two classes of genes.
3. Explain the "high fetal" mutation.
4. Use appropriately the vocabulary associated with this chapter when discussing its concepts.
5. Describe Cooley's anemia as it relates to gene activity.
6. Discuss how actinomycin D inhibits puff production.
7. Describe the relationship between hormones and gene action.

SELF-PRETEST OF LEARNING GOALS

Before proceeding further in the study of this chapter, attempt to answer the following questions without referring to other information. Upon completion of the test, compare your responses with the answer key at the end of the *Study Guide* chapter. Then correct the wrong responses by referring to the text (page numbers are indicated following each question).

True–False

1. Each new cell derived mitotically from the fertilized egg has exactly the same DNA content. (p. 351)
   a. True   b. False

2. Each specialized cell is unique in its protein content. (p. 351)
   a. True   b. False

3. Based on Jacob and Monod's hypothesis, an operon is a group of adjacent structural genes that are activated or deactivated by an operator locus. (p. 352)
   a. True   b. False

4. The studies of Jacob and Monod have led to the concept that there is only one class of gene. (p. 353)
   a. True   b. False

Matching

5. Jacob (p. 351)
6. Cooley (p. 355)
7. Britten (p. 356)
8. Balbiani (p. 357)
9. Beermann (pp. 358, 359)
10. Clever (p. 360)
11. Bonner (p. 361)

a. thalassemia, serious blood disorder
b. first observed giant chromosomes
c. operon hypothesis
d. proposed that each structural gene has at least one control gene
e. showed that puffs are localized sites of RNA synthesis
f. revealed that hormones influence puff formation
g. histone repression of nucleus

Fill in the Blank

12. Control genes have been divided into categories, the_____genes and the _____genes. (p. 353)

13. "High fetal" genes are associated with the production of fetal_____. (p. 353)

14. & 15. Several investigators have postulated that the above condition (question 13) is a genetic defect such that the _____ gene cannot be switched on and the_____ gene is permanently on. (pp. 353, 354)

16. The antibiotic known as_____is capable of inhibiting the production of chromosomal puffs. (p. 359)

17. The antibiotic mentioned in question 16 penetrates the cell and unites with the_____ molecule. (p. 359)

18. Evidence indicates that a protein known as_____forms a complex with DNA and enhances tight coiling by inhibiting the separation of the DNA strands. (p. 361)

VOCABULARY

These are key words that you should know. By learning these you will achieve learning goal number 4. The page where the respective definition occurs is indicated following the word.

1. operon (p. 351)
2. structural gene (p. 352)
3. control gene (p. 353)
4. "high fetal" gene (p 353)
5. Cooley's anemia (p.355)
6. beta and delta genes (p. 355)
7. giant chromosomes (p. 357)

8. *Drosophila* (p. 357)
9. chromosomal "puff" (p. 358)
10. actinomycin (p. 359)
11. lampbrush chromosome (p. 359)
12. ecdysone (p. 360)
13. histone (p. 361)

STUDY EXERCISES

Instructions: Write out your answers carefully and completely on a separate paper. Check your answers by referring to the text page indicated.

1. What is an operon? (p. 351)
2. Explain the genetic malfunction that causes Cooley's anemia (thalassemia). (p. 355)
3. Describe how a mutation of the operator gene causes a physiological malfunction. (p. 353)
4. What is a chromosomal puff? (p. 358)
5. What are lampbrush chromosomes? (p. 359)

SELF-POSTTEST OF LEARNING GOALS

Instructions: After completing the vocabulary and study exercises in written form it is now time to review. State each definition orally several times. Reread those areas in your text associated with the study exercises on which you did poorly. Retake the pretest at this time.

ANSWERS

1. a
2. a
3. a
4. b
5. c
6. a
7. d
8. b
9. e
10. f
11. g
12. operator; regulator
13. hemoglobin
14. beta
15. gamma
16. actinomycin D
17. DNA
18. histone

Chapter 22

Human Chromosomes and Autosomal Abnormalities

OVERVIEW

Only recently has the human chromosome number been definitely established at 46 (23 pairs) and techniques developed to do detailed study of human chromosomes during various stages of mitosis. Of these 23 pairs, 22 are termed *autosomal* and 1 is termed a *sex chromosome* pair. This chapter presents numerous human chromosomal abnormalities that will be of definite interest to you because you, just as all other humans, are subject to chromosome change.

LEARNING GOALS

After successfully completing this chapter you should, orally or in writing, be able to do the following.

1. State the number of human chromosomes.
2. Use appropriately the vocabulary associated with this chapter when discussing its concepts.
3. Explain the difference, chromosomally, between the human male and human female.
4. Describe how individual chromosomes can be identified in the laboratory.
5. Discuss the anatomical manifestations associated with Down's syndrome.
6. Explain the genetic reason for the condition of Down's syndrome.
7. State the cause of nondisjunction.
8. Describe the chromosomal error known as *translocation.*
9. Discuss the condition known as *chromosomal deletion* and describe the visible changes evident in the affected infant.
10. Relate leukemia to the abnormal chromosome known as the *Philadelphia chromosome.*

SELF-PRETEST OF LEARNING GOALS

Before proceeding further in the study of this chapter, attempt to answer the following questions without referring to other information. Upon completion of the test, compare your responses with the answer key at the end of the *Study Guide* chapter. Then correct the wrong responses by referring to the text (page numbers are indicated following each question).

True—False

1. Until only the late 1950s it was thought that the human chromosome number was 48. (p. 365)
   a. True   b. False

2. Colchicine is a plant extract that, when applied to human cells, arrests the process of mitosis. (p. 365)
   a. True   b. False

3. Phytohemagglutinin, a plant extract, causes human white blood cells to stop mitosis after prophase. (p. 367)
   a. True   b. False

4. Autosomes are abnormal chromosomes. (p. 368)
   a. True   b. False

Multiple Choice

5. Which of the following represents the normal sex chromosome pairing in the human male? (pp. 368, 369)
   a. XX   d. YY
   b. XO   e. YO
   c. XY   f. XXY

6. Which of the following represents the normal sex chromosome pairing in the human female? (p. 368)
   a. XX   d. YY
   b. XO   e. YO
   c. XY   f. XXY

7. In the human the 22 matching pairs of chromosomes are known as (p. 368)
   a. autosomes.   c. acrocentrosome.
   b. submetasome.   d. karosome.

8. Mongolism is also known as (p. 370)
   a. Down's syndrome.   c. Klinefelter's syndrome.
   b. Turner's syndrome.   d. none of these.

9. Which of the following are anatomically observable in Down's syndrome? (pp. 370, 372)
   a. Prominent forehead   d. Protruding tongue
   b. Flattened nasal bridge   e. All of these
   c. Habitually open mouth   f. All but one of these

10. Down's syndrome affects approximately how many infants every 600 births? (p. 371)
    a. 1   d. 20
    b. 12   e. 130
    c. 6   f. 222

11. If, during the first meiotic division, a given pair of homologous chromosomes fails to separate from each other, the abnormality is known as (pp. 373, 374)
    a. monosomy.   d. translocation.
    b. trisomy.   e. deletion.
    c. nondisjunction.   f. none of these.

12. When two chromosomes break and then rejoin in another combination, the condition is termed (p. 376)
    a. monosomy.   d. translocation.
    b. trisomy.   e. deletion.
    c. nondisjunction.   f. none of these.

13. Sometimes a piece of chromosome breaks off, resulting in (p. 378)
    a. monosomy.   d. translocation.
    b. trisomy.   e. deletion.
    c. nondisjunction.   f. none of these.

Matching

14. Nowell (p. 367)
15. Down (p. 370)
16. German (p. 375)
17. Ford (p. 376)
18. Painter (p. 365)
19. Lejeune (p. 378)

a. concluded that man had 48 chromosomes in every cell
b. observed that phytohemagglutinin stimulated leucocyte mitosis
c. mongolism
d. delayed fertilization proposal
e. observed first translocation error in humans
f. did research in chromosome deletion

VOCABULARY

These are key words or phrases that you should know. By learning these you will achieve learning goal number 2. The page where the respective definition occurs is indicated following the word or phrase.

1. colchicine (p. 365)
2. phytohemagglutinin (p. 367)
3. karyotype (p. 368)
4. metacentric (p. 368)
5. submetacentric (p. 368)
6. acrocentric (p. 368)
7. autosome (p. 368)
8. sex chromosome (p. 368)
9. tritium (p. 369)
10. Giemsa stain (p. 370)
11. Mongolism (p. 370)

12. trisomy (p. 372)
13. nondisjunction (p. 374)
14. monosomy (p. 374)
15. delayed fertilization (p. 375)
16. translocation (p. 376)
17. 15/21 translocation (p. 376)
18. deletion (p. 378)
19. Philadelphia chromosome (p. 379)
20. leukemia (p. 379)
21. cri du chat syndrome (p. 380)

STUDY EXERCISES

Instructions: Write out your answers carefully and completely on a separate paper. Check your answers by referring to the text page indicated.

1. Explain how new laboratory techniques enabled science to study human chromosomes. (pp. 365-370)
2. How do human male and female chromosomes differ? (p. 368)
3. Describe the general physical features of an infant suffering from Down's syndrome. (pp. 370, 372)
4. What is leukemia? (p. 379)
5. How do translocation and deletion compare and differ? (pp. 376, 378)

SELF-POSTTEST OF LEARNING GOALS

Instructions: After completing the vocabulary and study exercises in written form it is now time to review. State each definition orally several times. Reread those areas in your text associated with the study exercises on which you did poorly. Retake the pretest at this time.

ANSWERS

1. a	5. c	9. e	13. e	17. e
2. a	6. a	10. a	14. b	18. a
3. b	7. a	11. c	15. c	19. f
4. b	8. a	12. d	16. d	

Chapter 23

Sex Chromosome Abnormalities

OVERVIEW

Each animal cell contains a specific number of chromosome pairs in its nucleus. One pair of these chromosomes is designated as the sex chromosome (XX or XY), because certain genes on these chromosomes ultimately determine the anatomical configuration of the sex organs. The sex of an individual is determined at the moment the sperm and egg unite. There are certain sex chromosome abnormalities that result in a deviation from the normal female (XX) or normal male (XY) pairing. These will be discussed in this chapter. You should pay close attention to which of these abnormalities are fatal and to those that result in retardation.

LEARNING GOALS

After successfully completing this chapter you should, orally or in writing, be able to do the following.

1. Use appropriately the vocabulary associated with this chapter when discussing its concepts.
2. Describe the conditions associated with meiotic and mitotic nondisjunction.
3. Discuss the significance of the Barr body.
4. Explain genetic inactivation.

SELF-PRETEST OF LEARNING GOALS

Before proceeding further in the study of this chapter, attempt to answer the following questions without referring to other information. Upon completion of the test, compare your responses with the answer key at the end of the *Study Guide* chapter. Then correct the wrong responses by referring to the text (page numbers are indicated following each question).

Multiple Choice

1. Sex in the human is determined (p. 383)
   a. at implantation.
   b. at 6 weeks of development.
   c. at 12 weeks of development.
   d. none of these.

2. Which abnormal condition is associated with the XXY chromosome disorder? (p. 383)
   a. Klinefelter's syndrome
   b. Down's syndrome
   c. Turner's syndrome
   d. Barr syndrome

3. Which abnormal condition is associated with the XO chromosome disorder? (pp. 383, 384)
   a. Klinefelter's syndrome
   b. Down's syndrome
   c. Turner's syndrome
   d. Barr syndrome

4. Which of the following has the lowest incidence rate? (pp. 385, 386)
   a. Turner's syndrome
   b. Klinefelter's syndrome

True—False

5. A person with the chromosome arrangement XXX has a greater degree of mental abnormality than one with XXXX. (p. 383)
   a. True   b. False

6. A female with an XXX chromosome constitution can have a child who can be XX. (p. 386)
   a. True   b. False

7. Most true hermaphrodites have 46 chromosomes and an XX constitution. (p. 386)
   a. True   b. False

8. The greater the number of Barr bodies, the greater the number of X chromosomes. (p. 390)
   a. True   b. False

Matching

(Answers may be used more than once or not at all.) There may be more than one answer on some questions.

9. Klinefelter's syndrome (p. 383)
10. Turner's syndrome (p. 384)

   a. male patients are sterile
   b. most patients are sterile
   c. unable to menstruate
   d. subnormal intelligence
   e. incidence, 1 in 3,500
   f. incidence, 1 in 800

VOCABULARY

These are key words or phrases that you should know. By learning these you will achieve learning goal number 1. The page where the respective definition occurs is indicated following the word or phrase.

1. Klinefelter's syndrome (p. 383)
2. Turner's syndrome (p. 384)
3. selective disjunction (p. 386)
4. hermaphrodite (p. 386)
5. mosaic (pp. 386, 387)
6. mitotic nondisjunction (p. 387)
7. Barr body (pp. 389, 390)
8. triplo-X females (pp. 386, 390)
9. genetic inactivation (p. 390)

STUDY EXERCISES

Instructions: Write out your answers carefully and completely on a separate paper. Check your answers by referring to the text page indicated.

1. Explain Klinefelter's and Turner's syndromes. (pp. 383, 384)
2. What might cause the multiple X's condition in genetically abnormal humans? (p. 383)
3. What is the significance of the Barr body? (pp. 389-391)
4. Describe the difference between a mosaic and a hermaphrodite. (p. 386)
5. Briefly discuss mitotic nondisjunction. (p. 387)

PROBE

1. If a person is born a true hermaphrodite and surgery is to be utilized to remove one of the reproductive tissues, what factors are to be considered in determining the eventual sex of this infant?

SELF-POSTTEST OF LEARNING GOALS

Instructions: After completing the vocabulary and study exercises in written form it is now time to review. State each definition orally several times. Reread those areas in your text associated with the study exercises on which you did poorly. Retake the pretest at this time.

ANSWERS

1. d
2. a
3. c
4. a
5. b

6. a
7. a
8. a
9. a, b, f
10. b, c, d, e

Chapter 24

Sex-Linked Inheritance and Dosage Compensation

OVERVIEW

Previously, it was indicated to you that the normal human male and female had the sex chromosome pairing XY and XX, respectively. These two chromosomes contain the sex determining genes, but they are also associated with numerous traits that are not related to sexual development. The genes associated with the X chromosome are thus said to be *sex-linked*. To exemplify this, we see that in females a recessive gene on one X chromosome can be masked by its dominant allele on the other X chromosome. In males, genes on the one X chromosome produce an effect, since there is no other X chromosome present, only a Y chromosome. In general, sex-linked traits are exhibited by the male and transmitted by the female. In this chapter we will consider several of those sex-linked conditions that occur in the human population.

LEARNING GOALS

After successfully completing this chapter you should, orally or in writing, be able to do the following.

1. Use appropriately the vocabulary associated with this chapter when discussing its concepts.
2. Explain the genetics of sex-linked traits.
3. Discuss how hemophilia is transmitted.
4. Explain how hemorrhages can be checked in a person who is hemophilic.
5. Describe the genetic mechanism of color-blindness.
6. Discuss the sex-linked disorder known as *Duchenne muscular dystrophy*.
7. Describe the dosage compensation mechanism.
8. Explain the major points of Lyon hypothesis.
9. State how the Barr body is formed.
10. Describe the X-linked condition called *anhidrotic ectodermal dysplasia*.
11. Discuss sex-limited inheritance in the human using baldness as an example.

SELF-PRETEST OF LEARNING GOALS

Before proceeding further in the study of this chapter, attempt to answer the following questions without referring to other information. Upon completion of the test, compare your responses with the answer key at the end of the *Study Guide* chapter. Then correct the wrong responses by referring to the text (page numbers are indicated following each question).

True—False

1. The X chromosome is the principal carrier of sex-linked genes. (p. 395)
   a. True   b. False

2. Hemophilia is a disorder of the kidney. (p. 395)
   a. True   b. False

3. Hemophilia occurs only in human males. (p. 395)
   a. True   b. False

4. The human male has only one X sex chromosome and is said to be *hemizygous* for the X-linked gene. (p. 395)
   a. True   b. False

5. There is no known cure for hemophilia (p. 395)
   a. True   b. False

Fill in the Blank

6. The National Hemophilic Foundation estimates that hemophilia affects about_____ Americans. (p. 396)

7. The males afflicted with hemophilia in the royal families of Europe trace their ancestry to Queen _____of England. (p. 396)

8. The two colors_____and_____are of principal concern in X-linked color blindness. (p. 398)

9. The inactive X hypothesis has become known as the_____hypothesis. (p. 399)

10. It is evident that the inactivated X becomes condensed to form the_____body. (p. 399)

Matching

11. Lyon (p. 399)
12. Beutler (pp. 399, 400)
13. Turner (p. 401)
14. Shettles (p. 404)
15. Christmas (p. 396)

a. glucose-6-phosphate dehydrogenase
b. XO sex chromosome condition
c. inactive X hypothesis
d. detected two distinct sperm types
e. none of these

VOCABULARY

These are key words or phrases that you should know. By learning these you will achieve learning goal number 1. The page where the respective definition occurs is indicated following the word or phrase.

1. sex-linked genes (p. 395)
2. hemophilia (p. 395)
3. hemizygous (p. 395)
4. antihemophilic globulin (p. 396)
5. Christmas disease (p. 396)
6. Duchenne muscular dystrophy (p. 398)
7. Lyon hypothesis (p. 399)
8. dosage compensation (p. 399)
9. anhidrotic ectodermal dysplasia (p. 399)

STUDY EXERCISES

Instructions: Write out your answers carefully and completely on a separate paper. Check your answers by referring to the text page indicated.

1. Explain a sex-linked trait. (p. 395)
2. Why does hemophilia occur almost exclusively in males? (p. 395)
3. Briefly describe the anatomical aspects of Duchenne's muscular dystrophy. (p. 398)
4. What is genetic dosage compensation? (p. 399)

5. Describe the main thrust of the Lyon hypothesis. (p. 399)
6. What abnormality does a person who has anhidrotic ectodermal dysplasia exhibit? (p. 399)
7. Why is baldness considered a sex-limited inheritance? (p. 402)

PROBE

1. Present arguments for and against parents being able to regulate the sex of their offspring.

SELF-POSTTEST OF LEARNING GOALS

Instructions: After completing the vocabulary and study exercises in written form it is now time to review. State each definition orally several times. Reread those areas in your text associated with the study exercises on which you did poorly. Retake the pretest at this time.

ANSWERS

1. a
2. b
3. b
4. a
5. a
6. 100,000
7. Victoria
8. red, green

9. Lyon
10. Barr
11. c
12. a
13. b
14. d
15. e

Chapter 25

Genetic Engineering and Genetic Counseling

OVERVIEW

Man has for many years yearned for the knowledge that would allow him to control a gene and ultimately the synthesis of a specific enzyme. In recent years scientists have unraveled the genetic code, synthesized DNA, and isolated pure genes. The major advances remaining for science are in the field of gene manipulation. There must occur the ability to remove DNA molecules and replace these molecules with previously synthesized ones. By doing this many hereditary, chemical, or viral-induced chromosomal abnormalities could be corrected. Naturally, one of the major reasons for this type of scientific endeavor is to alleviate needless human suffering. At present, we are able to counsel persons concerning the risks of occurence and the recurrence of inherited disorders. This chapter presents materials that will allow you to observe the advances in these genetic areas and the need for much research in other genetic areas.

LEARNING GOALS

After successfully completing this chapter you should, orally or in writing, be able to do the following.

1. Use appropriately the vocabulary associated with this chapter when discussing its concepts.
2. Explain how transduction occurs between bacterial cells when selected viral units are present.
3. State the characteristics of the disorder agammaglobulinemia.
4. State the greatest obstacle in organ transplantation.
5. Describe the two important ingredients of a successful genetic counseling.
6. Explain the cause of Tay-Sachs disease.
7. Describe the technique known as *transabdominal amniocentesis*.
8. State an opinion concerning therapeutic abortions.

SELF-PRETEST OF LEARNING GOALS

Before proceeding further in the study of this chapter, attempt to answer the following questions without referring to other information. Upon completion of the test, compare your responses with the answer key at the end of the *Study Guide* chapter. Then correct the wrong responses by referring to the text (page numbers are indicated following each question).

Fill in the Blank

1. The process by which a virus mediates the transfer of bacterial genes from one bacterial cell to the

    next bacterial cell it invades is termed _____ . (p. 407)

2. _____ is a disorder characterized by a deficiency or lack of antibodies. (p. 409)

3. _____ disease is a fatal, untreatable cerebral degenerative disorder characterized by large quantities of fatty material being deposited in brain cells. (p. 411)

4. Removal of sample amniotic fluid from the area surrounding a developing fetus within the uterus of the mother, by a technique known as _____, affords analysis that can result in establishing if the embryo contains certain abnormal genes. (p. 412)

True—False

5. Normally, when a virus enters a bacterial cell, it multiplies within that cell. (p. 407)
   a. True   b. False

6. The phenomenon of transduction was first observed by Dr. James Langley in 1951. (p. 407)
   a. True   b. False

7. Viruses do not contain DNA. (p. 408)
   a. True   b. False

8. Transplantation of bone marrow in leukemia has not proven rewarding. (p. 409)
   a. True   b. False

9. The greatest obstacle in organ transplantation is graft rejection based on genetic incompatibilities between donor and host. (p. 409)
   a. True   b. False

10. Height and weight are expressions of polygenes. (pp. 409, 410)
    a. True   b. False

11. There are only 11 genetic counseling centers in the United States at present. (p. 410)
    a. True   b. False

12. In almost every genetic disorder there are more carriers than there are those who exhibit the disorder. (p. 410)
    a. True   b. False

13. Any program designed to curtail birth deformities must be based on the voluntary cooperation of each couple. (p. 414)
    a. True   b. False

VOCABULARY

These are key words or phrases that you should know. By learning these you will achieve learning goal number 1. The page where the respective definition occurs is indicated following the word or phrase.

1. transduction (p. 407)
2. agammaglobulinemia (p. 409)
3. cystinosis (p. 409)
4. quantitative character (p. 409)
5. polygene (p. 410)
6. genetic counseling (pp. 410, 411)
7. Tay-Sachs disease (p. 411)
8. transabdominal amniocentesis (p. 412)
9. therapeutic abortion (pp. 413, 414)

STUDY EXERCISES

Instructions: Write out your answers carefully and completely on a separate paper. Check your answers by referring to the text page indicated.

1. Explain how transduction can occur. (pp. 407, 408)
2. Describe the advantage of utilizing transabdominal amniocentesis. (pp. 413, 414)

PROBE

1. Should genetic counseling become an integral part of a physician's academic training?
2. Present arguments for and against the use of therapeutic abortions to eliminate embryos that are doomed to death shortly after birth.
3. Suppose you are a prospective parent and pregnancy is in the sixth week. At this time the physician and/or genetic counselor relate to you that both you and your spouse are carriers of a fatal condition. Further analysis confirms that the developing embryo has Tay-Sachs disease. Explain what your decision would be and why you selected this avenue regarding the fate of the developing offspring. (See pages 411 and 412 for background on Tay-Sachs disease.)

SELF-POSTTEST OF LEARNING GOALS

Instructions: After completing the vocabulary and study exercises in written form it is now time to review. State each definition orally several times. Reread those areas in your text associated with the study exercises on which you did poorly. Retake the pretest at this time.

ANSWERS

1. transduction
2. agammaglobulinemia
3. Tay-Sachs disease
4. transabdominal amniocentesis
5. a
6. b
7. b

8. a
9. a
10. a
11. b
12. a
13. a

Chapter 26

Darwinian Scheme of Evolution

OVERVIEW

Man has always concerned himself with ideas and theories about where living things came from. Most theories were based on myth rather than the results of scientific endeavors. Not until Charles Darwin presented the concept of natural selection in 1859 did man begin to truly explore the phenomenon of evolution. Darwin's theory has been enriched and refined by advances of modern science in many fields of biology, chemistry, and geology. To understand evolution one must understand that the word simply means gradual change. No modern evolutionist claims to understand all facets of the mechanism by which the process occurs, but no one would argue that change does not occur. Darwin's theory of natural selection is in this chapter and affords you the opportunity to observe step by step how this important scheme was developed.

LEARNING GOALS

After successfully completing this chapter you should, in writing or orally, be able to do the following.

1. Use appropriately the vocabulary associated with this chapter when discussing its concepts.
2. Describe the pronouncement of Archbishop Ussher.
3. Relate how Darwin came to be a member of the ship named the *Beagle*.
4. State the arguments presented by Charles Lyell that influenced Darwin's thinking.
5. Describe the findings of Darwin when he visited Argentina.
6. State where the Galápagos Islands are located.
7. Discuss Darwin's observations of the land-dwelling tortoise and finches in the Galápagos Islands.
8. Explain the phylogenetic tree as constructed by Darwin.
9. State the basic suppositions of Darwin when he returned home to England in 1836 as they relate to selection.
10. Identify the single ancestor of all domestic chickens.
11. Explain Lamarck's theory of inheritance of acquired characteristics.
12. Briefly describe the major thrust of Malthus' book, *Essay on the Principle of Population*.
13. Discuss the influence of Alfred Wallace on Darwin as it relates to the initial presentation of the concept of natural selection and ultimately to his *Origin of Species*.
14. Explain the basic process of the survival of the fittest as proposed in Darwin's natural selection.
15. Discuss the process known as *industrial melanism*.

SELF-PRETEST OF LEARNING GOALS

Before proceeding further in the study of this chapter, attempt to answer the following questions without referring to other information. Upon completion of the test, compare your responses with the answer key at the end of the *Study Guide* chapter. Then correct the wrong responses by referring to the text (page numbers are indicated following each question).

Fill in the Blank

1. _____is a term that means "an unfolding" and suggests gradual change. (p. 421)

2. In 1831 Charles Darwin accepted the post of naturalist on board the ship, H.M.S. _____. (p. 421)

3. Darwin's voyage on this ship lasted from 1831 until 18_____. (p. 422)

4. Archbishop_____pronounced that all organisms were created precisely at 9:00 a.m. on Sunday, October 23, in 4004 B.C. (p. 422)

5. The book *Principles of Geology,* authored by_____impressed Darwin and altered his thoughts concerning natural forces shaping the geologic past. (p. 422)

6. Darwin spent much time in the South American country_____observing bones of extinct mammals. (pp. 422, 424)

7. Settlers from_____ brought with them to South America the modern horse, *Equus.* (p. 424)

8. Darwin studied the giant land-dwelling tortoise and small finch (bird) while visiting the _____Islands, located 600 miles west of Ecuador in the Pacific Ocean. (p. 425)

9. _____was the man who constructed a phylogenetic tree and placed it in his book, *Origin of Species.* (p. 426)

10. The scientific name of the ancestor of all domestic chickens is_____. (p. 427)

11. _____was the French naturalist who proposed the theory of inheritance of acquired characteristics. (p. 428)

12. _____was the English clergyman who wrote *Essay on the Principles of Population,* which greatly influenced Darwin. (p. 429)

13. If it had not been for a fellow naturalist named_____pursuing the idea of natural selection, Darwin may never have published his selection concepts. (p. 430)

True—False

14. Because of natural selection, no one group of organisms swarms uncontrollably over the surface of the earth. (p. 431)
    a. True   b. False

15. "Survival of the fittest" actually refers to natural selection. (p. 431)
    a. True   b. False

16. Populations of organisms are continuously subject to natural selection. (p. 433)
    a. True   b. False

17. In England the peppered moth has changed from a light-colored specimen to a dark, or melanic, one because of the adaptation necessary to survive the environmental changes brought on by the English industrial revolution. (pp. 434, 435)
    a. True   b. False

18. The two varieties of moths (light and melanic) differ principally by a group of six genes. (p. 435)
    a. True   b. False

VOCABULARY

These are key words or phrases that you should know. By learning these you will achieve learning goal number 1. The page where the respective definition occurs is indicated following the word or phrase.

1. evolution (p. 421)
2. H.M.S. *Beagle* (p. 421)
3. Archbishop Ussher (p. 422)
4. Charles Lyell (p. 422)
5. Galápagos Islands (p. 425)
6. *Equus* (p. 424)
7. *Toxodon* (p. 424)
8. *Origin of Species* (p. 421)
9. *Gallus gallus* (p. 427)
10. Jean de Lamarck (p. 428)
11. Thomas Malthus (pp. 429, 430)
12. mercantilism (p. 429)
13. natural selection (p. 430)
14. industrial melanism (pp. 433, 434)

STUDY EXERCISES

Instructions: Write out your answers carefully and completely on separate paper. Check your answers by referring to the text page indicated.

1. Relate how Darwin came to propose his theory of natural selection. (pp. 426-429)
2. Explain how industrial melanism occurred. (pp. 433-435)
3. Explain Darwin's phylogenetic tree. (p. 426)

SELF-POSTTEST OF LEARNING GOALS

Instructions: After completing the vocabulary and study exercises in written form it is now time to review. State each definition orally several times. Reread those areas in your text associated with the study exercises on which you did poorly. Retake the pretest at this time.

ANSWERS

1. evolution
2. *Beagle*
3. 36
4. Ussher
5. Lyell
6. Argentina
7. Spain
8. Galápagos
9. Darwin
10. *Gallus gallus*
11. Lamarck
12. Malthus
13. Wallace
14. a
15. a
16. a
17. a
18. b

Chapter 27

Genetic Variation and Mutation

OVERVIEW

With an understanding of the mechanisms of heredity as stated by Mendel, researchers began to recognize that fields of biology could be studied not as separate entities, but as compatable components of science. All individuals represent thousands of traits. Each trait is genetically passed from generation to generation unless genetic variation occurs. When a trait mutates, the structure of the gene changes and, thus, the generation to follow will be like its parent, but may be different from its far-removed ancestor. In many organisms, under specific conditions, certain combinations of genes are more advantageous than others. Darwin's natural selection favors only the more beneficial gene combinations. This chapter weaves the classical work of Mendel and Darwin with that of current researchers to provide you with an in-depth presentation of genetic variation and mutation.

LEARNING GOALS

After successfully completing this chapter you should, orally or in writing, be able to do the following.

1. State the relationship between background radiation and spontaneous mutations.
2. Describe the discovery of Hermann Muller that genes are susceptible to the action of X rays.
3. Discuss the somatic consequences of exposure to the 1945 World War II atomic blasts in Japan.
4. State the relationship between whole body exposure to radiation at high dose levels and the incidence of leukemia.
5. Explain why the effectiveness of certain antibiotic agents has been reduced.
6. State the chance a zygote will carry one newly mutated gene contributed by either the sperm or egg cell.
7. Explain the doubling dose as it relates to genetic mutations.
8. Discuss whether or not all mutations are harmful.
9. Use appropriately the vocabulary associated with this chapter when discussing its concepts.

SELF-PRETEST OF LEARNING GOALS

Before proceeding further in the study of this chapter, attempt to answer the following questions without referring to other information. Upon completion of the test, compare your responses with the answer key at the end of the *Study Guide* chapter. Then correct the wrong responses by referring to the text (page numbers are indicated following each question).

True—False

1. Darwin recognized that the process of evolution is inseparably linked to the mechanism of inheritance. (p. 439)
   a. True
   b. False

2. All differences in the genes of organisms have their origin in mutation. (p. 439)
   a. True
   b. False

3. Once a mutation occurs that same mutation cannot repeat itself. (p. 439)
   a. True   b. False

4. The amount of background radiation is too low to account for all spontaneous mutations. (pp. 439, 440)
   a. True   b. False

5. X rays cause only genetic damage, not somatic damage. (pp. 440, 441)
   a. True   b. False

6. Atomic bomb blasts at the end of World War II in Japan demonstrated that Japanese women in early pregnancy (less than 15 weeks) exposed to the blast at a distance less than 1.3 miles from the center ultimately produced many somatically damaged offspring. (pp. 440, 441)
   a. True   b. False

7. There is no relationship between whole body exposure to radiation at high dose levels and the incidence of leukemia. (p. 441)
   a. True   b. False

8. Streptomycin is an antibiotic agent. (p. 442)
   a. True   b. False

Fill in the Blank

9. The effectiveness of certain antibiotics has been reduced by the emergence of resistant strains of _____. (p. 442)

10. In 1927, the late scientist_____discovered that genes are highly susceptible to the action of X rays. (p. 440)

11. _____was the scientist who presented evidence that antibiotics act as selecting agents permitting preexisting mutations to express themselves. (p. 443)

Multiple Choice

12. Which of the following are antibiotics? (p. 442)
    a. Penicillin   c. Streptomycin
    b. Sulfonamides   d. All of these

13. The chance that an egg cell containing a newly mutated gene will be fertilized by a sperm carrying a new mutant gene is (p. 447)
    a. 1 in 16.   d. 1 in 1,000.
    b. 1 in 3.   e. 1 in 10,000.
    c. 1 in 100.

14. Estimates indicate that if all causes of human embryo death are collectively presented,_____ percent of the embryos fail to survive *in utero*. (p. 448)
    a. 30   d. 5
    b. 20   e. 2
    c. 15

15. The increase in radiation necessary to double the mutation rate is known as the (p. 448)
    a. lethal dose.   d. retard dose.
    b. fatal dose.   e. none of these.
    c. doubling dose.

16. All mutations are (pp. 449, 450)
    a. harmful.
    b. beneficial.
    c. inferior in some environments, superior in others.
    d. produced only when advantageous.

VOCABULARY

These are key words or phrases that you should know. By learning these you will achieve learning goal number 9. The page where the respective definition occurs is indicated following the word or phrase.

1. mutation (p. 439)
2. roentegens (p. 440)
3. somatic radiation damage (p. 440)
4. genetic radiation damage (pp. 441, 442)
5. antibiotic (p. 442)
6. replica plating (p. 443)
7. doubling dose (p. 448)
8. *Daphnia* (p. 449)

STUDY EXERCISES

Instructions: Write out your answers carefully and completely on separate paper. Check your answers by referring to the text page indicated.

1. Describe the work of Herman Muller as it relates to radiation effects on genes. (pp. 440-442)
2. Discuss what somatic effects were observed following the World War II atomic bomb blast at Hiroshima and Nagasaki. (pp. 440, 441)
3. What has reduced the effectiveness of antibiotics such as penicillin? (pp. 442, 443)
4. Describe the harmful nature of mutations. (pp. 449, 450)

SELF-POSTTEST OF LEARNING GOALS

Instructions: After completing the vocabulary and study exercises in written form it is now time to review. State each definition orally several times. Reread those areas in your text associated with the study exercises on which you did poorly. Retake the pretest at this time.

ANSWERS

1. a
2. a
3. b
4. a
5. b
6. a
7. b
8. a
9. bacteria
10. Muller
11. Lederberg
12. d
13. a
14. a
15. c
16. c

Chapter 28

Concept of Genetic Equilibrium

OVERVIEW

Genetics, the science of heredity, can deal with DNA, genes, chromosomes, or an entire population. Breeding activities greatly influence the genetic composition of a population. Random mating occurs when any individual has an equal opportunity of pairing with any other individual. It is the intent of this chapter to present materials that will allow you to understand genetic equilibrium.

LEARNING GOALS

After successfully completing this chapter you should, orally or in writing, be able to do the following.

1. Use appropriately the vocabulary associated with this chapter when discussing its concepts.
2. Explain random mating.
3. Describe the symptoms of acatalasia.
4. Discuss the relationship between genetic equilibrium and the Hardy-Weinberg law.
5. Relate the use of *p* and *q* in observing the frequency of genes in a population.
6. Describe the results observed when the Hardy-Weinberg principle is applied to acatalasia in Japan.
7. State the frequency of albinos in human populations.
8. State the frequency of heterozygous carriers of albinism in the human population.

SELF-PRETEST OF LEARNING GOALS

Before proceeding further in the study of this chapter, attempt to answer the following questions without referring to other information. Upon completion of the test, compare your responses with the answer key at the end of the *Study Guide* chapter. Then correct the wrong responses by referring to the text (page numbers are indicated following each question).

True—False

1. Random mating occurs when any female can mate with any male in the population. (p. 453)
   a. True   b. False

2. Persons who have the dominant trait known as *acatalasia* lack the enzyme catalase. (p. 453)
   a. True   b. False

3. The chance that two independent events will occur together is the product of their chances of occurring separately. (p. 454)
   a. True   b. False

4. If parents have the genotypes *Aa* and *Aa,* two out of four offspring would be expected to have the same genotype. (p. 455)
   a. True   b. False

5. A population in which the proportions of genotypes remain unchanged from generation to generation is said to be in equilibrium. (p. 456)
   a. True   b. False

6. The Hardy-Weinberg law requires that random mating be present for equilibrium to remain constant. (p. 457)
   a. True   b. False

7. The Hardy-Weinberg law is theoretical. (p. 458)
   a. True   b. False

8. When the Hardy-Weinberg law is stated mathematically p is the frequency of one gene while q denotes the allele. (p. 457)
   a. True   b. False

9. The Hardy-Weinberg equilibrium is not applicable to acatalasia in Japan because the condition is the result of three different mutant alleles. (p. 458)
   a. True   b. False

Multiple Choice

10. The frequency of albinos in the human population is (p. 458)
    a. 1/20,000.   c. 1/2,000,000.
    b. 1/100,000.   d. 1/650,000.

11. The frequency of heterozygous carriers of albinism in the human population is (p. 459)
    a. 1/200.   d. 1/1,000.
    b. 1/10.   e. 1/20,000.
    c. 1/70.

VOCABULARY

These are key words or phrases that you should know. By learning these you will achieve learning goal number 1. The page where the respective definition occurs is indicated following the word or phrase.

1. random mating (p. 453)
2. acatalasia (p. 453)
3. Hardy-Weinberg law (pp. 456, 457)

STUDY EXERCISES

Instructions: Write out your answers carefully and completely on separate paper. Check your answers by referring to the text page indicated.

1. Explain random mating. (p. 453)
2. Describe the Hardy-Weinberg law. (pp. 456, 457)
3. Why isn't the Hardy-Weinberg equilibrium applicable to acatalasia in the Japanese population? (p. 458)

SELF-POSTTEST OF LEARNING GOALS

Instructions: After completing the vocabulary and study exercises in written form it is now time to review. State each definition orally several times. Reread those areas in your text associated with the study exercises on which you did poorly. Retake the pretest at this time.

ANSWERS

1. a
2. b
3. a
4. a
5. a
6. a
7. a
8. a
9. a
10. a
11. c

Chapter 29

Concept of Selection

OVERVIEW

If a trait is classified as completely dominant and a disorder occurs only in the recessive state, the heterozygote carrier cannot be distinguished from the normal homozygote noncarrier. It is therefore impossible to eliminate the carrier; carriers simply cannot be identified. The material of this chapter is designed to acquaint you with the relationship of selection and the elimination of deleterious mutant genes.

LEARNING GOALS

After successfully completing this chapter you should, orally or in writing, be able to do the following.

1. Describe the change in the incidence of a recessive fatal trait through three generations.
2. Discuss the interplay of mutation and selection.
3. Compare the reduction in the incidence of a recessive lethal, semilethal, and subvital gene after 20 generations.
4. Explain selection coefficient.
5. State how the equilibrium frequency of a detrimental dominant gene in a population can be altered.
6. State how many concealed lethal genes the average person harbors.
7. Use appropriately the vocabulary associated with this chapter when discussing its concepts.
8. Describe Muller's plan, called *AID*.

SELF-PRETEST OF LEARNING GOALS

Before proceeding further in the study of this chapter, attempt to answer the following questions without referring to other information. Upon completion of the test, compare your responses with the answer key at the end of the *Study Guide* chapter. Then correct the wrong responses by referring to the text (page numbers are indicated following each question).

Multiple Choice

1. If one observes three generations with random mating employed, what reduction in the incidence of a recessive trait would you expect? (p. 465)
   a. 25%
   b. 15%
   c. 50%
   d. 4%
   e. 2%

2. With complete (lethal) selection, a reduction in the incidence of the recessive trait from 1.0 percent to 0.25 percent is accomplished in _____ generations. (p. 469)
   a. 10
   b. 9
   c. 25
   d. 6
   e. 2

3. When the recessive gene is semilethal, a reduction in the incidence of the recessive trait from 1.0 percent to 0.25 percent is accomplished in_____generations. (p. 469)
   a. 10
   b. 6
   c. 20
   d. 25
   e. 2

4. A_____recessive gene is one that, in double dose, impairs an individual to the extent that his reproductive fitness is less than 100% but more than 50% of normal proficiency. (p. 468)
   a. lethal
   b. semilethal
   c. subvital
   d. none of these

True—False

5. The selection coefficient is a measure of the contribution of one genotype relative to the contributions of the other genotypes. (p. 469)
   a. True
   b. False

6. The equilibrium frequency of the detrimental dominant gene in a population cannot be altered by changing the rate of loss of the gene in question. (p. 471)
   a. True
   b. False

7. It can be safely stated that every human individual contains at least one newly mutated gene. (p. 472)
   a. True
   b. False

8. The average person is said to harbor four concealed lethal genes. (p. 472)
   a. True
   b. False

9. Theodosius Dobzhansky proposed the *AID* plan. (p. 473)
   a. True
   b. False

10. All geneticists agree that the human species is deteriorating genetically. (p. 474)
    a. True
    b. False

VOCABULARY

These are key words or phrases that you should know. By learning these you will achieve learning goal number 7. The page where the respective definition occurs is indicated following the word or phrase.

1. lethal selection (p. 468)
2. lethal, semilethal, and subvital genes (p. 468)
3. consanguineous marriage (p. 472)
4. Muller's *AID* plan (pp. 472, 473)

STUDY EXERCISES

Instructions: Write out your answers carefully and completely on separate paper. Check your answers by referring to the text page indicated.

1. Describe Hermann Muller's *AID* plan. (pp. 472-474)
2. Differentiate between lethal, semilethal, and subvital recessive genes. (p. 468)

PROBE

1. Present arguments for and against the immediate sterilization of an individual carrying deleterious genes. (background material on pages 472-474)

SELF-POSTTEST OF LEARNING GOALS

Instructions: After completing the vocabulary and study exercises in written form it is now time to review. State each definition orally several times. Reread those areas in your text associated with the study exercises on which you did poorly. Retake the pretest at this time.

ANSWERS

1. d
2. a
3. c
4. c
5. a

6. b
7. a
8. a
9. b
10. b

Chapter 30
Selection and Infectious Diseases

OVERVIEW

Man existed as a nomadic hunter for thousands of years. Only recently has man been able to form communities, domesticate animals and easily travel from country to country or continent to continent. His mating patterns and way of life have drastically changed in the last century. However, with all the advances man has made, he is still susceptible to infectious diseases caused by bacterial and viral agents. While man's evolution moves at a slow pace, these microorganisms can respond to their environment by mutating, and man's best selection techniques cannot control this rapid genetic change. In this chapter, various infectious diseases will be presented. Likewise, genetic changes and selection of these organisms will be observed.

LEARNING GOALS

After successfully completing this chapter you should, orally or in writing, be able to do the following.

1. Use appropriately the vocabulary associated with this chapter when discussing its concepts.
2. Describe how, experimentally, it was shown that selection favors the emergence of less virulent strains of a pathogen that causes a fatal disease.
3. Explain, based on experiments by Fenner, how natural selection favored a mutual accommodation between the myxomatosis virus and the Australian rabbit.
4. Discuss laboratory experiments that demonstrate how genetic resistance to disease can occur, utilizing the typhoid pathogen *Salmonella typhimurium*. Repeat the discussion and use the Plains Indian and tuberculosis as examples of genetic resistance to disease.
5. Indicate whether a bacteria or virus causes tuberculosis, bubonic plague, measles, mumps, chicken pox, and smallpox.
6. State when an infectious disease tends to reach epidemic proportions.
7. Explain how tuberculosis can be transmitted.
8. State what has caused the reduction in mortality of persons infected with tuberculosis.
9. Give the current annual occurrence of tuberculosis and drugs used as therapeutic agents.
10. Describe how the bacterial disease bubonic plague received its name.
11. Discuss various historical aspects of bubonic plague.
12. Explain the relationship between bubonic and pneumonic plague.
13. State the approximate numbers of persons affected by malaria each year throughout the world.
14. State the cause of malaria.
15. Describe the symptoms exhibited by a person infected by the malarian parasite.
16. Indicate where, geographically, malaria predominantly occurs in the world.
17. Explain the relationship between the female *Anopheles* mosquito and the *Plasmodium* protozoa.

SELF-PRETEST OF LEARNING GOALS

Before proceeding further in the study of this chapter, attempt to answer the following questions without referring to other information. Upon completion of the test, compare your responses with the answer key at the end of the *Study Guide* chapter. Then correct the wrong responses by referring to the text (page numbers are indicated following each question).

Matching

1. Fenner (p. 477)
2. Haldane (p. 479)
3. Dubos (p. 480)

a. studied myxomatosis selection
b. suggested that infectious diseases were one of the most potent agents of natural selection of man in the past
c. studied ethnic selection for tuberculosis

True—False

4. Myxomatosis is caused by a virus. (p. 477)
   a. True
   b. False

5. In any fatal disease, selection would not favor the emergence of less virulent strains. (p. 481)
   a. True
   b. False

6. Experimentation by the Australian scientist, Fenner, using rabbits, demonstrated that genetic resistance to a virus occurs. (p. 478)
   a. True
   b. False

7. It was shown that natural selection has favored a mutual accommodation between the myxomatosis virus and the Australian rabbit. (p. 478)
   a. True
   b. False

8. Typhoid is caused by *Salmonella typhimurium*. (p. 478)
   a. True
   b. False

Matching (Answers may be used more than once.)

9. Tuberculosis (pp. 480, 481)
10. Smallpox (p. 479)
11. Bubonic plague (p. 481)
12. Mumps (p. 479)
13. Pneumonic plague (p. 482)

a. bacteria
b. virus

Multiple Choice

14. What is the annual number of cases of tuberculosis at present? (p. 481)
    a. 20/100,000
    b. 200/100,000
    c. 2,000/100,000
    d. 20,000/100,000

15. What is the annual number of cases of malaria at present? (p. 482)
    a. 350,000
    b. 35,000
    c. 3,500,000
    d. 350,000,000

16. Which of the following is used to treat tuberculosis chemotherapeutically? (p. 481)
    a. INH
    b. Penicillin
    c. Streptomycin
    d. Tetracycline

True–False

17. Tuberculosis is a moderately contagious disease. (p. 480)
    a. True   b. False

18. Plains Indians have developed a genetic resistance to tuberculosis. (p. 480)
    a. True   b. False

19. An infectious disease tends to reach epidemic proportions in populations that have had no previ-
    ous exposure to the disease. (p. 480)
    a. True   b. False

20. Tuberculosis is transmitted via the air through minute droplets of sputum. (pp. 480-481)
    a. True   b. False

Fill in the Blank

21. Malaria is caused by the protozoa _____. (pp. 482, 483)

22. Bubonic plague is transmitted from rat to man by a bacteria. When this same bacteria is transmit-
    ted from human to human the disease is termed the_____plague. (p. 482)

23. Bubonic plague received its name because an acutely inflamed node is technically called a
    _____. (p. 481)

24. The Black Death (bubonic plague) killed approximately_____million people in the 14th
    century. (p. 482)

VOCABULARY

These are key words or phrases that you should know. By learning these you will achieve learning goal
number 1. The page where the respective definition occurs is indicated following the word or phrase.

1. myxomatosis (p. 477)   5. passive immunity (p. 479)
2. attenuated (p. 478)   6. tuberculosis (pp. 480, 481)
3. *Salmonella typhimurium* (p. 478)   7. bubonic plague (pp. 481, 482)
4. typhoid (p. 479)   8. malaria (pp. 482, 483)

STUDY EXERCISES

Instructions: Write out your answers carefully and completely on separate paper. Check your answers
by referring to the text page indicated.

1. Describe the various methods used by the Australian government in an attempt to control the
    increased rabbit population. (p. 477)
2. Discuss the Plains Indians from 1881 through 1950 with respect to the incidence of tuberculosis.
    (p. 480)
3. Describe, historically, how the bubonic plague affected the people of Europe. (pp. 481, 482)
4. Explain the relationship between the female *Anopheles* mosquito and the protozoan, *Plasmodium*.
    (p. 483)

SELF-POSTTEST OF LEARNING GOALS

Instructions: After completing the vocabulary and study exercises in written form it is now time to review. State each definition orally several times. Reread those areas in your text associated with the study exercises on which you did poorly. Retake the pretest at this time.

ANSWERS

1. a
2. b
3. c
4. a
5. b
6. a
7. a
8. a
9. a
10. b
11. a
12. b
13. a
14. a
15. d
16. a
17. b
18. a
19. a
20. a
21. *Plasmodium*
22. pheumonic
23. bubo
24. 25

Chapter 31

Balanced Polymorphism

OVERVIEW

As we have already seen, not all mutant genes are detrimental. Likewise, not all abnormal genes are eliminated rapidly by the selection process. One such example is the mutant gene that causes the disease sickle-cell anemia. For deleterious genes to occur generation after generation in populations requires a selective mechanism that results in a population structure known as *balanced polymorphism*. This chapter provides a detailed analysis of this selective mechanism.

LEARNING GOALS

After successfully completing this chapter you should, orally or in writing, be able to do the following.

1. Use appropriately the vocabulary associated with this chapter when discussing its concepts.
2. State the genotype of an individual with sickle-cell anemia and that of a carrier of the sickle-cell trait.
3. Account for the high incidence of the sickle-cell gene in many parts of the world.
4. Briefly describe balanced polymorphism.
5. Discuss the work of Sheppard as it relates to the ability of a lethal gene to be maintained at a stable relatively high frequency.
6. Explain what might be the selective advantage of the sickle-cell trait over the normal.
7. State how the spread of malaria is associated with the spread of the selective advantage of the sickle-cell gene.
8. State the frequency of the sickle-cell trait among American Negroes.
9. State how many generations are necessary for the incidence of the heterozygous carrier of sickle-cell anemia to be depressed.
10. State the genotype of a person having erythroblastosis fetalis.
11. Provide the possible offspring genotypes if a heterozygous father and homozygous recessive mother had four children.
12. State the relationship between human blood groups and the susceptibility to certain common diseases.

SELF-PRETEST OF LEARNING GOALS

Before proceeding further in the study of this chapter, attempt to answer the following questions without referring to other information. Upon completion of the test, compare your responses with the answer key at the end of the *Study Guide* chapter. Then correct the wrong responses by referring to the text (page numbers are indicated following each question).

Multiple Choice

1. Sickle-cell anemia is a (p. 487)
   a. homozygous trait.
   b. heterozygous trait.

2. Which of the following represents the genotype of a carrier of sickle-cell anemia? (p. 487)
   a. $Hb^S Hb^S$
   b. $Hb^S Hb^s$
   c. $Hb^s Hb^s$
   d. None of these

3. Which of the following is an explanation for the high level of incidence of the sickle-cell gene? (p. 487)
   a. $Hb^S Hb^S$ is superior to $Hb^S Hb^s$ and $Hb^s Hb^s$.
   b. $Hb^S Hb^s$ is superior to $Hb^S Hb^S$ and $Hb^s Hb^s$.
   c. $Hb^s Hb^s$ is superior to $Hb^S Hb^S$ and $Hb^S Hb^s$.

4. Which of the following statements is true with respect to the selective advantage of the heterozygous sickle-cell anemic African over the normal homozygote? (p. 491)
   a. Heterozygotes are more susceptible to anemia.
   b. Heterozygotes are less susceptible to malaria.
   c. Heterozygotes have increased lung capacity.
   d. None of these

5. Which of the following genotypes represent the erythroblastotic infant? (p. 493)
   a. *RR*
   b. *Rr*
   c. *rr*
   d. None of these

True—False

6. Sickle-cell anemic individuals are usually derived from the marriage of two homozygotes. (p. 487)
   a. True
   b. False

7. Generally persons with sickle-cell anemia do not survive to reproductive age. (p. 487)
   a. True
   b. False

8. The sickle-cell trait has been found in Africa, United States, Greece, and the Near East. (pp. 487, 493)
   a. True
   b. False

9. Balanced polymorphism occurs when selective forces serve to maintain two alleles at completely different frequencies in a population. (p. 489)
   a. True
   b. False

10. Sheppard, utilizing the fruit fly, demonstrated that a lethal gene can be maintained at a stable, relatively high frequency in a population. (p. 490)
    a. True
    b. False

11. Sheppard's experiments allowed the heterozygote to have an advantage over the homozygote. (p. 490)
    a. True
    b. False

12. The selective advantage of the sickle-cell heterozygote tends to increase in direct proportion to the amount of malaria present in a given area. (p. 492)
    a. True
    b. False

13. The highest frequencies of the sickle-cell gene occur consistently in regions relatively free of malaria. (p. 492)
    a. True
    b. False

Multiple Choice

14. The frequency of the sickling trait among American Negroes is approximately_____per-
    cent. (p. 493)
    a. 50   d. 25
    b. 72   e. 1
    c. 9

15. Regarding the sickle-cell trait, how many generations are required for the incidence of the hetero-
    zygous carrier to be depressed from 18 to 6.5 percent? (p. 493)
    a. 100   d. 30
    b. 200   e. 5
    c. 60

16. If a heterozygote (*Rr*) marries a homozygous recessive (*rr*), how many of four children would you
    expect to be heterozygous? (p. 494)
    a. 1   c. 3
    b. 2   d. 4

17. Which of the following blood group types are at least 40 percent more prone to develop duodenal
    ulcers? (p. 494)
    a. A   c. AB
    b. B   d. O

VOCABULARY

These are key words or phrases that you should know. By learning these you will achieve learning goal
number 1. The page where the respective definition occurs is indicated following the word or phrase.

1. balanced polymorphism (p. 487)   3. *Anopheles gambiae* (p. 492)
2. *Plasmodium falciparum* (p. 491)   4. erythroblastosis fetalis (p. 493)

STUDY EXERCISES

Instructions: Write out your answers carefully and completely on separate paper. Check your answers
by referring to the text page indicated.

1. What is balanced polymorphism? (pp. 489, 490)
2. Relate Sheppard's experimentation to sickle-cell anemia. (pp. 490, 491)
3. Briefly discuss the association between human blood groups and their susceptibility to certain
   common diseases. (p. 494)

PROBE

1. If two black Americans, each being a heterozygote (carrier) for the sickle-cell trait, were thinking
   of marriage, should they be warned that 1 of 4 children could have the disease? Present arguments
   for and against any marriage involving carriers that could result in sickle-cell anemia, brain defects,
   or erythroblastosis fetalis.

SELF-POSTTEST OF LEARNING GOALS

Instructions: After completing the vocabulary and study exercises in written form it is now time to review. State each definition orally several times. Reread those areas in your test associated with the study exercises on which you did poorly. Retake the pretest at this time.

ANSWERS

1. a
2. b
3. b
4. b
5. b
6. b
7. a
8. a
9. b

10. a
11. a
12. a
13. b
14. c
15. d
16. b
17. d

Chapter 32

Genetic Drift and Gene Flow

OVERVIEW

America has been called "the melting pot" of the world because of the influx of immigrants from almost every other country in the world. Likewise, marriage across ethnic lines has abounded for years. Today, if you ask the "average" American about their background, they answer, "I am part Dutch, part German, part this, or part that." This leads to the point already made that harmful recessive genes in a population are generally carried by the heterozygote. The probability in the human population that two heterozygotes will mate is directly proportional to the size of the population in which they live. Therefore, if marriage in America does not occur on any ethnic or religious basis, then the chance of two heterozygotes for a given trait marrying are much less than if marriage occurred among a small ethnic group of, for example, 2,000 people. If the population is small then the chance of the recessive gene appearing is great. There are several small religious populations in the United States (such as the Dunkers and the Amish) that will be explored. In this chapter causes of genetic drift and gene flow will be presented, thus allowing you the opportunity to observe the influence of population size.

LEARNING GOALS

After successfully completing this chapter you should, orally or in writing, be able to do the following.

1. Describe the Sewall Wright effect as it relates to the random drift of gene frequencies from generation to generation in a small population.
2. Explain what influence the founder effect has on the establishment of a new population via migration.
3. State the incidence of albinism among the North American Indians and European Caucasians.
4. State which blood group is most prominent among North American Indians.
5. Discuss, based on Woolf's theory, why the incidence of albinism has been maintained at such a high level among Hopi Indians.
6. Describe the study of the Dunker community by Bentley Glass and compare the gene frequency of selected traits in this community to that in the general American population.
7. State whether rare recessive traits occur in greater numbers in small isolated populations or among the large general population.
8. Describe the recessive disorders that occur with uncommonly high frequencies among the Amish.
9. State why hemolytic disease, until recently, was virtually unknown in China.
10. State the long-range effect of Chinese-American intermarriages on the incidence of hemolytic disease of the newborn.
11. State the percentage of the Caucasian contribution to the American Negro gene pool.
12. Relate the frequency of the Duffy factor among Caucasians, African Negroes, and American Negroes.
13. Compare the derivation of genes from Caucasian stock by American Negroes in New York, Detroit, and Charleston.
14. Use appropriately the vocabulary associated with this chapter when discussing its concepts.

SELF-PRETEST OF LEARNING GOALS

Before proceeding further in the study of this chapter, attempt to answer the following questions without referring to other information. Upon completion of the test, compare your responses with the answer key at the end of the *Study Guide* chapter. Then correct the wrong responses by referring to the text (page numbers are indicated following each question).

Multiple Choice

1. To whom would the following concept be attributed: the gene pool of the new generation may not be at all representative of the parental gene pool from which it was drawn? (p. 498)
   a. Wright
   b. Glass
   c. Goin
   d. Fledberg
   e. Inwood

2. The unique frequencies of genes that arise in populations derived from small bands of colonizers is termed the (p. 500)
   a. Wright effect.
   b. Graves drift.
   c. founder effect.

3. Which of the following blood groups is most prominent among North American Indians? (p. 500)
   a. B
   b. A
   c. O
   d. AB
   e. AO

4. What is the incidence of albinism among European Caucasians? (p. 500)
   a. 1 in 100
   b. 1 in 1,000
   c. 1 in 10,000
   d. 1 in 20,000

5. Which of the following statements reflects Woolf's findings concerning albinism among Hopi Indians? (p. 501)
   a. There have been no albino males found, only females.
   b. Albinsim is recessive and has never occurred among the Hopi tribe.
   c. The incidence of albinism is high because albinos rank high in Hopi society and males have enjoyed success is sexual activity.
   d. Albinos have occurred but were isolated, thus "freezing" the recessive gene.
   e. None of these

6. The frequency of Caucasian genes among American Negroes in New York and Detroit is (p. 507)
   a. 10 percent.
   b. 26 percent.
   c. 70 percent.
   d. 50 percent.

True—False

7. Shifts in gene frequencies in large populations are determined almost exclusively by selection. (p. 503)
   a. True
   b. False

8. A study of the Dunker community by Bentley Glass indicates that the O blood group in these people occurs more frequently than among the general population. (p. 502)
   a. True
   b. False

9. Small, isolated groups have a greater occurrence of rare recessive traits than would be expected from random mating in a large population. (p. 503)
   a. True
   b. False

10. In Amish communities marriages are mainly among close relatives and such recessive disorders as the Ellis—van Creveld syndrome and the Troyer syndrome occur with uncommonly high frequencies. (pp. 503, 504)
   a. True   b. False

11. The long-range effect of Chinese-American intermarriages is an increase in the incidence of hemolytic disease of the newborn. (p. 506)
   a. True   b. False

12. Between 1850 and 1950, 60 percent of the Chinese population carried recessive genes (*Rr*) for hemolytic diseases. (p. 506)
   a. True   b. False

13. The Duffy blood factor is much higher among African Negro populations as compared with the American Negro population. (pp. 506, 507)
   a. True   b. False

VOCABULARY

These are key words or phrases that you should know. By learning these you will achieve learning goal 14. The page where the respective definition occurs is indicated following the word or phrase.

1. genetic drift (p. 498)
2. Sewall Wright effect (p. 498)
3. founder effect (p. 500)
4. cultural selection (p. 501)
5. religious isolates (pp. 501-505)

STUDY EXERCISES

Instructions: Write out your answers carefully and completely on a separate paper. Check your answers by referring to the text page indicated.

1. Why has the incidence of albinism remained high among Hopi Indians? (p. 501)
2. Why is there a difference between the northern and southern American Negro with respect to the percentage of genes derived from the Caucasians? (pp. 506, 507)

SELF-POSTTEST OF LEARNING GOALS

Instructions: After completing the vocabulary in written form it is now time to review. State each definition orally several times. Reread those areas in your text associated with the study exercises on which you did poorly. Retake the pretest at this time.

ANSWERS

1. a
2. c
3. c
4. d
5. c
6. b
7. a

8. b
9. a
10. a
11. b
12. b
13. b

Chapter 33

Polygenic Inheritance and Intelligence

OVERVIEW

A typical monohybrid cross utilizing simple Mendelian inheritance divides a trait into two clearly distinguishable groups. The appearance of either group is due to a single pair of genes associated with a respective chromosome pair. Many traits occur as the result of the action of many genes (polygenes). This interaction of genes, resulting in quantitative traits, will be discussed in this chapter.

LEARNING GOALS

After successfully completing this chapter you should, orally or in writing, be able to do the following.

1. Use appropriately the vocabulary associated with this chapter when discussing its concepts.
2. Describe the polygenic inheritance of quantitative traits.
3. Explain Nilsson-Ehle's postulate concerning kernel color in wheat.
4. Write the genotype for a completely homozygous and a completely heterozygous trihybrid.
5. Based on Davenport's observation, explain the genetic difference between a West African Negro and a Caucasian.
6. Write the genotype for black skin, white skin, and mulatto skin.
7. Solve specific genetic problems involving skin color and height.
8. State the law of filial regression.
9. Describe the change in human stature during the past century.
10. State what, other than the additive effect of polygenes, influences height in a population.
11. State what the Binet test actually measures.
12. Explain how an IQ is determined.
13. Indicate whether Galton's earlier prediction concerning a decline in the average level of intelligence has been shown to be correct or incorrect.
14. State what factors have been postulated that could account for the difference in intelligence among black and white Americans.

SELF-PRETEST OF LEARNING GOALS

Before proceeding further in the study of this chapter, attempt to answer the following questions without referring to other information. Upon completion of the test, compare your responses with the answer key at the end of the *Study Guide* chapter. Then correct the wrong responses by referring to the text (page numbers are indicated following each question).

True—False

1. All quantitative traits are polygenic. (p. 511)
   a. True
   b. False

2. Skin color is a quantitative trait. (p. 511)
   a. True
   b. False

3. The inheritance of height is nonquantitative. (p. 511)
   a. True   b. False

4. The law of filial regression was stated by Galton. (pp. 516, 517)
   a. True   b. False

5. If height is the trait being observed and the genotype of the father is *AABB,* three sperm (gamete) types are possible. (p. 517)
   a. True   b. False

6. Homogamy results when like individuals do not elect to mate. (p. 519)
   a. True   b. False

Matching

7. Davenport (p. 514)
8. Nilsson-Ehle (p. 512)
9. Galton (pp. 516, 517)
10. Binet (pp. 521, 522)

a. studied the inheritance of kernel color in wheat as an example of polygenic effect
b. made extensive observations on the outcome of Negro-Caucasian marriages in Jamaica
c. law of filial regression
d. devised "intelligence test"

Multiple Choice

11. Which of the following human traits is/are the result of polygenic inheritance? (p. 511)
    a. Height   d. All of these
    b. Weight   e. None of these
    c. Skin color

12. Based on the Nilsson-Ehle postulate, kernel color is an additive effect resulting from the association of how many gene pairs? (p. 512)
    a. 2   d. 5
    b. 3   e. 6
    c. 4

13. Which of the following represents a completely homozygous trihybrid? (p. 512)
    a. *AABBCC*   e. Two of these
    b. *aabbcc*   f. None of these
    c. *AaBbCc*   g. *aaBBCc*
    d. *AABbCc*

14. Which of the following represents a completely heterozygous trihybrid? (p. 512)
    a. *AaBBcc*   d. *AaBbCc*
    b. *AaBbCC*   e. *aabbCc*
    c. *AABBCC*

15. Which of the following represents the genotype for skin color in the Negro? (p. 514)
    a. *AABB*   d. *Aabb*
    b. *aabb*   e. None of these
    c. *aaBb*

16. Which of the following represents the genotype for Caucasian skin color? (p. 514)
    a. *AABB*   d. *Aabb*
    b. *aabb*   e. None of these
    c. *aaBb*

17. Based on Davenport's hypothesis, what skin color would be the result of a mating between a black-skinned Negro and a Caucasian? (p. 514)
    a. Black
    b. Dark brown
    c. Mulatto
    d. Light brown
    e. White

18. If a black-skinned Negro (*AABB*) married a Caucasian (*aabb*), and if they had a child who in turn married a Caucasian (*aabb*), how many children of four would you expect to be black? (p. 514) The solution is found on page 119 of *Study Guide*.
    a. 0
    b. 1
    c. 2
    d. 3
    e. 4

19. Based on the information in question 18, how many children of four would you expect to be white? (p. 514) The solution is found on page 119 of the *Study Guide*.
    a. 0
    b. 1
    c. 2
    d. 3
    e. 4

20. Which of the following statements would be associated with the law of filial regression? (p. 517)
    a. Progeny of extreme variants tend to be like the most extreme variant.
    b. Progeny of extreme variants tend to be a little in excess of the most extreme variant.
    c. Progeny of extreme variants tend to return towards the average of the population.
    d. None of these

21. During the past century in most industrial societies the average height of the human population has increased by approximately how many inches? (p. 519)
    a. 0
    b. .25
    c. 1.5
    d. 3.0
    e. 5.0

22. Which of the following influences height in a population? (pp. 519-521)
    a. Genetic composition
    b. Homogamy
    c. Environment
    d. Two of these
    e. None of these
    f. All of these

23. Which of the following is an accurate statement concerning the test devised by Alfred Binet in 1905? (p. 522)
    a. This test indicates that intelligence is totally genetic.
    b. This test is a general measure of academic readiness.
    c. This test uses 125 as a median intelligence level.
    d. This test indicates the maturity outcome of an individual.

True—False

24. All persons of average intelligence have an IQ of 100. (pp. 522, 523)
    a. True
    b. False

25. IQ is derived by dividing a child's mental age by his chronological age and multiplying by 100. (p. 523)
    a. True
    b. False

26. Galton predicted that as man advanced following the industrial revolution, his level of intelligence would increase by 3 percent each generation. (p. 525)
    a. True
    b. False

27. IQ tests serve almost exclusively to illuminate cultural differences. (p. 528)
    a. True   b. False

28. IQ tests have been designed for Caucasian populations. (p. 528)
    a. True   b. False

29. It appears likely that environmental factors can account for most, if not all, of the differences in mean IQ scores between black Americans and white Americans. (p. 528)
    a. True   b. False

30. American blacks, descendants of involuntary immigrants from Africa, have, in general, developed different attitudes, values, and expectations than whites. (pp. 527, 528)
    a. True   b. False

VOCABULARY

These are key words or phrases that you should know. By learning these you will achieve learning goal number 1. The page where the respective definition or phrase occurs is indicated following the word or phrase.

1. quantitative trait (p. 511)   7. IQ (pp. 522, 523)
2. polygenic action (p. 511)   8. correlation coefficient (p. 523)
3. mulatto (p. 514)   9. dizygotic twin (p. 524)
4. mean (p. 514)   10. sibling (p. 525)
5. law of filial regression (p. 517)   11. Caucasian (p. 527)
6. homogamy (p. 519)

STUDY EXERCISES

Instructions: Write out your answers carefully and completely on a separate paper. Check your answers by referring to the text page indicated.

1. What is polygenic inheritance? (p. 511)
2. What is the basic difference, genetically, between the Negro native to West Africa and a Caucasian? (p. 514)
3. Describe how a mulatto phenotype might occur. (p. 514)
4. Briefly state several reasons why human stature has increased steadily during the past century in most industrial societies. (pp. 519-521)
5. Specifically, what does the Binet test measure? (p. 522)
6. What are several reasons why black Americans have, in general, a lower IQ score than white Americans? (pp. 527-528)

PROBLEM SOLUTIONS (Questions 18 and 19 on pretest)

Stated: Black-skinned Negro has $AABB$ genotype
         Caucasian has $aabb$ genotype

Parents (P_1): $AABB$ × $aabb$
Gametes: AB × ab
Child (F_1): $AaBb$

Page 514 of the text indicates that $AaBb$ has a medium-brown or mulatto skin color. In a mating of black-skinned Negro and a Caucasian *every* child will be $AaBb$ (mulatto).

Stated: The child (*AaBb*) at maturity married a Caucasian (*aabb*).
Genotypes: *AaBb* x *aabb*
Gametes: *AB, Ab, aB, ab (ab)*

Punett square:

	ab	
AB	AaBb	medium-brown (mulatto)
Ab	Aabb	light brown
aB	aaBb	light brown
ab	aabb	white

Question 18 asked how many children in a family of four would have black skin; the answer, as you can see, is *none*.

Question 19 asked how many children in a family of four would have white skin; the answer is *one* (*aabb*).

Additional Material on Skin Color

A. General Statements
1. All children from two black-skinned parents (*AABB*) will be black.
2. All children from two white-skinned parents (*aabb*) will be white.
3. All children from one black parent and one white parent will have medium-brown skin (*mulatto*).

B. Problems
1. Is it possible to have a black-skinned grandparent and a white-skinned parent?
   Grandparents: *AABB* x *aabb*
   Parents: *AaBb* x *aabb*
   Child: *aabb*
   Answer: Yes, you could have white skin and have a grandparent with black skin.

2. Is it possible for two medium-brown-skinned persons (mulattos) to have either black or white children? That is to say, could brothers and sisters have different shades of skin?
   Parents: *AaBb* x *AaBb*
   Gametes: *AB, Ab, aB (ab)* *AB, Ab, aB (ab)*

Solution:

	AB	Ab	aB	ab
AB	AABB	AABb	AaBB	AaBb
Ab	AABb	AAbb	AaBb	Aabb
aB	AaBB	AaBb	aaBB	aaBb
ab	AaBb	Aabb	aaBb	aabb

AABB = Black
aabb = White

Answer: Yes, you would expect 1 of 16 offspring to be black and 1 of 16 to be white, or stated another way, 1 of 8 would be expected to be either black or white. You will observe the many other skin shades possible when two *AaBb*s have children.

119

SELF-POSTTEST OF LEARNING GOALS

Instructions: After completing the vocabulary in written form it is now time to review. State each definition orally several times. Reread those areas in your test associated with the study exercises on which you did poorly. Retake the pretest at this time.

ANSWERS

1. a
2. a
3. b
4. a
5. b
6. b
7. b
8. a
9. c
10. d
11. d
12. b
13. e
14. d
15. a
16. b
17. c
18. a
19. b
20. c
21. c
22. f
23. b
24. b
25. a
26. b
27. a
28. a
29. a
30. a

Chapter 34

Races and Species

OVERVIEW

This planet on which we live is divided into polar regions, continents, and oceans. Each specified area has living organisms unique to that area and organisms that occur planet-wide. Adaptations have occurred that enable certain organisms to survive while others perish. We can thus observe that genetic differences relate to environmental conditions. This chapter attempts to answer the questions concerning how a population maintains its genetic distinctness, and what the consequences of free interchange and restricted exchange of genes between populations are.

LEARNING GOALS

After successfully completing this chapter you should, orally or in writing, be able to do the following.

1. Use appropriately the vocabulary associated with this chapter when discussing its concepts.
2. Explain a cline and a race.
3. Describe how a species can be formed.
4. Show how each and every organism is taxonomically classified, utilizing the binomial system.
5. List seven isolating mechanisms that prevent interbreeding.
6. Explain how a mule is produced.
7. State the species and three great divisions of modern man.

SELF-PRETEST OF LEARNING GOALS

Before proceeding further in the study of this chapter, attempt to answer the following questions without referring to other information. Upon completion of the test, compare your responses with the answer key at the end of the *Study Guide* chapter. Then correct the wrong responses by referring to the text (page numbers are indicated following each question).

Fill in the Blank

1. The term _____ is applied to situations for which a character varies more or less continuously with a gradual change in the environmental terrain. (p. 533)

2. Populations with well-marked discontinuities that are aggregrations and differ in the incidence of genetic traits are termed _____. (p. 534)

3. Two populations separated geographically are said to be _____. (p. 538)

4. A _____ is a breeding community that preserves its genetic identity by its inability to exchange genes with other such breeding communities. (p. 538)

5. The technical name of an organism consists of the _____ followed by its species name. (p. 538)

6. The binomial system of nomenclature or classification, now universally accepted, was devised by the Swedish naturalist whose last name was _____ (p. 539)

7. Two populations that come to occupy the same territory are called _____. (p. 539)

8. The ways or agencies that prevent interbreeding of sympatric species are known as reproductive _____ mechanisms. (p. 539)

9. The genus and species of modern man is _____. (p. 542)

10. Man can be classified as having three great divisions, the _____, the _____, and the _____. (p. 542)

11. A _____ is a reproductive community of individuals occupying a definite region. (p. 542)

12. The offspring produced as a result of mating between a female horse (mare) and a male jackass is sterile and termed a _____. (p. 540)

Matching

13. Seasonal isolation (p. 540)
14. Sexual isolation (p. 540)
15. Mechanical isolation (p. 540)
16. Gametic isolation (p. 540)

a. breeding at different times of the year
b. lack of mutual attraction between sexes of two species
c. external sexual apparatus of one species is physically incompatible with the genitalia of the other species
d. sperm cells of one species may be inviable in the reproductive tract of the female

VOCABULARY

These are key words or phrases that you should know. By learning these you will achieve learning goal number 1. The page where the respective definition occurs is indicated following the word or phrase.

1. cline (p. 533)
2. race (pp. 534, 535, 542)
3. allopatric (p. 538)
4. species (p. 538)
5. genus (p. 538)
6. Linnaeus (p. 539)
7. sympatric (p. 539)
8. reproductive isolating mechanisms (p. 539)

STUDY EXERCISES

Instructions: Write out your answers carefully and completely on a separate paper. Check your answers by referring to the text page indicated.

1. How can a species be formed? (pp. 536-538)
2. Explain the binomial system of nomenclature. (pp. 538, 539)
3. List the chief reproductive isolating mechanisms. (p. 539)
4. How do races and species differ? (pp. 534, 535, 538)

SELF-POSTTEST OF LEARNING GOALS

Instructions: After completing the vocabulary in written form it is now time to review. State each definition orally several times. Reread those areas in your text associated with the study exercises on which you did poorly. Retake the pretest at this time.

ANSWERS

1. cline
2. races
3. allopatric
4. species
5. genus
6. Linnaeus
7. sympatric
8. isolating

9. *Homo sapiens*
10. Caucasoid, Mongoloid, Negroid
11. race
12. mule
13. a
14. b
15. c
16. d

Chapter 35

Adaptive Radiation

OVERVIEW

Man, like many other animals, continually seeks shelter and food. Although the days of Neanderthal and other prehistoric, nomadic men has long since passed, modern man, *Homo sapiens,* continues to seek new places to live, where competition is reduced. Much of modern man's change has been from the inner city to the suburbs. Lesser animals move in much the same manner. Their survival, on a different level from man's, represents the major driving force in seeking a new environment. By selecting a new environment where competition for resources is low, new species may emerge from ancestral stock. Organisms, by nature, tend to adapt to their environment, and this adaptation may require change in the organism resulting in a new and better species.

LEARNING GOALS

After successfully completing this chapter you should, orally or in writing, be able to do the following.

1. Use appropriately the vocabulary associated with this chapter when discussing its concepts.
2. State the geographic location of the Galápagos Islands.
3. Describe the animals that inhabit the Galápagos Islands.
4. Discuss the basic differences among the finches on the Galápagos Islands, as observed by Darwin.
5. Explain how so many different finches could survive on the Galápagos Islands.
6. Describe the present genus classification of the finches on the Galápagos Islands.
7. Describe adaptive radiation.

SELF-PRETEST OF LEARNING GOALS

Before proceeding further in the study of this chapter, attempt to answer the following questions without referring to other information. Upon completion of the test, compare your responses with the answer key at the end of the *Study Guide* chapter. Then correct the wrong responses by referring to the text (page numbers are indicated following each question).

True—False

1. The Galápagos Islands are located in the Pacific, west of Ecuador. (p. 547)
   a. True   b. False

2. There are at least 85 different kinds of birds on the Galápagos Islands. (p. 547)
   a. True   b. False

3. The only place inhabited by the marine iguana, other than the Galápagos Islands, is New Zealand. (p. 547)
   a. True   b. False

4. Darwin's finches descended from seed-eating birds that inhabited the mainland of South America. (p. 549)
    a. True   b. False

5. The most striking differences among the finches on the Galápagos Islands are their legs. (p. 549)
    a. True   b. False

6. The absence of competition is a prime factor promoting adaptive radiation. (p. 551)
    a. True   b. False

7. All finches in the Galápagos Islands are related to one another. (p. 555)
    a. True   b. False

8. The ground and tree finches in the Galápagos Islands belong to the same genus. (p. 555)
    a. True   b. False

9. The spreading of populations into different environments, accompanied by divergent adaptive changes of the emigrant populations, is referred to as *adaptive radiation*. (p. 547)
    a. True   b. False

VOCABULARY

These are key words or phrases that you should know. By learning these you will achieve learning goal number 1. The page where the respective definition occurs is indicated following the word or phrase.

1. adaptive radiation (p. 547)
2. Galápagos Islands (p. 547)
3. marine iguana (p. 547)
4. *Geospiza* (pp. 554, 555)
5. *Camarhynchus* (pp. 554, 555)

STUDY EXERCISES

Instructions: Write out your answers carefully and completely on separate paper. Check your answer by referring to the text page indicated.

1. What is adaptive radiation? (p. 547)
2. Describe the plant and animal life present on the Galápagos Islands. (pp. 547-550)
3. Where are the Galápagos Islands located geographically? (p. 547)
4. What specific adaptations have Darwin's finches made, so as to be able to survive in the Galápagos Islands? (pp. 547-551)

SELF-POSTTEST OF LEARNING GOALS

Instructions: After completing the vocabulary in written form it is now time to review. State each definition orally several times. Reread those areas in your text associated with the study exercises on which you did poorly. Retake the pretest at this time.

ANSWERS

1. a
2. a
3. b
4. a
5. b

6. a
7. a
8. b
9. a

Chapter 36

Major Adaptive Radiations

OVERVIEW

The previous chapter demonstrated how Darwin's finches adapted to conditions on the Galápagos Islands. It is apparent this same adaptive mechanism has been in effect for millions of years. Organisms constantly seize new opportunities presented when competition is eliminated or environmental changes occur. As would be expected, the larger the region and the greater the diversity of the environment, the more abundant the variety of plant and animal species. This chapter presents material that will allow you to observe the process of adaptive radiation on a large scale. It begins approximately 400 million years ago during the Devonian period, when the vast areas of land were almost void of animal life.

LEARNING GOALS

After successfully completing this chapter you should, orally or in writing, be able to do the following.

1. Use appropriately the vocabulary associated with this chapter when discussing its concepts.
2. Cite when the Devonian geologic period occurred.
3. State the name and general characteristics of the Devonian aquatic fish from which the amphibians were derived.
4. Describe Romer's hypothesis concerning the formation of the amphibian.
5. Explain preadaptations.
6. Give several examples of modern descendants from ancient amphibians.
7. State how egg deposition differs between modern amphibians and reptiles.
8. State the name of the earliest and most primitive reptile and when they appeared.
9. Give the name of the group from which the dinosaur descended.
10. Cite the two great groups of dinosaurs.
11. Give the name of the reptile that could fly and the name of the thecodontian descendant that gave rise to the modern bird.
12. Describe several reptiles that returned to the water.
13. Discuss Dollo's law.
14. Explain the relationship between the pelycosaurs and the therapsids.
15. Describe the reversal of magnetic field theory as stated by internationally known oceanographer Bruce Heezen.
16. State when mammals arose to unquestionable dominance.
17. Give examples of marine mammals.
18. Compare the bone structure of the bat, human, and whale.
19. Describe the evolution of the horse.
20. State the name of the modern form of the horse.

SELF-PRETEST OF LEARNING GOALS

Before proceeding further in the study of this chapter, attempt to answer the following questions without referring to other information. Upon completion of the test, compare your responses with the answer key at the end of the *Study Guide* chapter. Then correct the wrong responses by referring to the text (page numbers are indicated following each question).

Matching

1. Crossopterygii (p. 559)
2. Salamander (p. 562)
3. Cotylosaur (p. 562)
4. Thecodont (p. 563)
5. Pterosaur (p. 563)
6. Plesiosaur (p. 565)
7. *Equus* (p. 568)

   a. lobe-finned fish
   b. forerunner of dinosaur
   c. modern amphibian
   d. earliest and most primitive reptile
   e. ancient reptile (marine)
   f. ancient reptile (flying)
   g. modern horse

Fill in the Blank

8. Approximately 400 million years ago, during the geologic period known as the _____, there were vast areas of land barren of animal life. (p. 559)

9. The _____ were ancient, air-breathing fishes and represent the stock from which the amphibians were derived. (p. 559)

10. _____ was the person who advanced the theory that the organisms mentioned in question 9 were forced to crawl on dry land when the pools they inhabited became foul, stagnant, or completely dry. (p. 559)

11. If an organism were to possess certain capacities that would prove to be important under new conditions of life, the potential would be termed _____. (p. 560)

12. The earliest and most primitive reptiles were known as the _____. (p. 562)

13. These reptiles (question 12) first appeared in the _____ period about 300 million years ago. (p. 562)

14. The dinosaur descended from the _____, which was a slender, fast-running, lizard-like creature. (p. 563)

True—False

15. Before the close of the Devonian period the transition from fish to amphibian had been completed. (p. 562)
   a. True   b. False

16. A frog is a reptile. (p. 562)
   a. True   b. False

17. Amphibians, like reptiles, lay their eggs in water. (p. 562)
   a. True   b. False

18. The Pennsylvanian period occurred approximately 600 million years ago. (p. 562)
   a. True   b. False

19. All dinosaurs were immense creatures. (p. 563)
   a. True   b. False

20. Dollo's law is associated with the irreversibility of evolution. (p. 565)
    a. True   b. False

21. Pelycosaurs gave rise to the therapsids. (p. 566)
    a. True   b. False

22. The reptilian dynasty collapsed before the close of the Mesozoic era. (p. 566)
    a. True   b. False

23. The reversal of magnetic field theory was stated by Heezen. (p. 566)
    a. True   b. False

24. The whale, dolphin, walrus, and seal are mammals. (p. 566)
    a. True   b. False

25. Mammals arose to dominance during the Cenzoic era. (p. 566)
    a. True   b. False

26. In a comparison of mammalian arm or leg structure, the structural design, bone for bone, is basically the same. (p. 567)
    a. True   b. False

27. The ancestry of horses can be traced back to the Devonian period. (pp. 566, 568-570)
    a. True   b. False

28. The modern horse was first introduced to North America in the early 1500s by the Spaniards. (p. 570)
    a. True   b. False

29. The two great groups of dinosaurs were the Saurischia and *Archaeopteryx*. (p. 563)
    a. True   b. False

30. The wing of a bird and the wing of a butterfly are homologous. (p. 568)
    a. True   b. False

VOCABULARY

These are key words or phrases that you should know. By learning these you will achieve learning goal number 1. The page where the respective definition occurs is indicated following the word or phrase.

1. Devonian geologic period (p. 559)
2. Crossopterygii (p. 559)
3. preadaptation (p. 560)
4. *Diplovertebron* (p. 562)
5. Cotylosaur (p. 562)
6. Pennsylvanian geologic period (p. 562)
7. Mesozoic geologic era (p. 562)
8. *Tyrannosaurus* (p. 563)
9. *Brontosaurus* (p. 563)
10. thecodonts (p. 563)
11. Saurischia (p. 563)
12. Ornithischia (p. 563)
13. *Archaeopteryx* (p. 565)
14. Dollo's law (p. 565)
15. Pelycosaurs (p. 565)
16. homologous (p. 568)
17. analogous (p. 568)
18. *Hyracotherium* (p. 568)
19. *Equus* (p. 568)

STUDY EXERCISES

Instructions: Write out your answers carefully and completely on a separate paper. Check your answers by referring to the text page indicated.

1. Relate how the dinosaur arose and eventually became extinct. Include approximate dates when major events occurred. (pp. 562-563)
2. Briefly describe the evolution of horses. (pp. 568-570)
3. Specifically, how do amphibians and reptiles differ? (p. 562)

SELF-POSTTEST OF LEARNING GOALS

Instructions: After completing the vocabulary in written form it is now time to review. State each definition orally several times. Reread those areas in your text associated with the study exercises on which you did poorly. Retake the pretest at this time.

ANSWERS

1. a	16. b
2. c	17. b
3. d	18. b
4. b	19. b
5. f	20. a
6. e	21. a
7. g	22. a
8. Devonian	23. a
9. Crossopterygii	24. a
10. Romer	25. a
11. preadaptation	26. a
12. cotylosaurs	27. b
13. Pennsylvanian	28. b
14. thecodont	29. b
15. a	30. b

Chapter 37

Origin and History of Life

OVERVIEW

The previous chapter established that this planet is very old. In fact, the movement toward a land-dwelling vertebrate began 400 million years ago. The thought patterns of the vast majority of the persons alive today do not allow for the comprehension of time in units as large as a million years. The time of the dinosaur spans 100 million years. Neither of these figures seem so impressive when we realize that the age of this planet Earth is between 4 and 5 billion years. Conditions on the planet at that time were much different than what is observed today. The first molecules formed in that period of time, so long ago, were spontaneously produced from chemical elements and ions present. This chapter presents materials that illustrate how the first molecules were made, how the first compounds arose, and, lastly, when a cell became a practical self-duplicating unit.

LEARNING GOALS

After successfully completing this chapter you should, orally or in writing, be able to do the following.

1. Explain the theory of Oparin concerning the transformation of lifeless chemicals into living matter.
2. State the estimated age of the Earth.
3. Describe the atmosphere of the primitive Earth.
4. Discuss how complex organic molecules could have been formed in this primitive environment.
5. State who was responsible for first synthesizing the organic compound urea.
6. Identify other organic compounds that have been artificially synthesized.
7. Describe the experimentation concerning artificial organic synthesis carried out by Stanley Miller in 1953 and Sidney Fox in 1964.
8. Discuss the composition of the sea during the primitive stage.
9. Describe how primitive autotrophs obtained their energy.
10. Identify the gaseous end product of photosynthesis.
11. Describe how the metabolic processes of the primitive anaerobic autotrophs influenced the evolution of green plants.
12. Distinguish between eucaryotic and procaryotic cells.
13. Describe a fossil.
14. State how fossils aid in the dating of period in the development of plant and animal life on this planet.
15. Describe the five main geologic eras and their respective geologic periods.
16. Discuss the structure of the psilophytes.
17. Describe the tree-sized plants of the carboniferous times.
18. State which animals have been fossilized in the deep Cambrian rocks.
19. Identify the animals that lived in early Paleozoic and Mesozoic waters.
20. State the estimated number of living insect species.
21. Describe how during the course of evolution plant and animal groups interacted to each other's advantage.
22. Use appropriately the vocabulary associated with this chapter when discussing its concepts.

SELF-PRETEST OF LEARNING GOALS

Before proceeding further in the study of this chapter, attempt to answer the following questions without referring to other information. Upon completion of the test, compare your responses with the answer key at the end of the *Study Guide* chapter. Then correct the wrong responses by referring to the text (page numbers are indicated following each question).

Matching

1. Oparin (p. 573)
2. Wöhler (p. 574)
3. Miller (p. 574)
4. Fox (p. 574)

a. author of *The Origin of Life*
b. synthesized protein under extreme heat
c. first to artificially produce urea
d. synthesized organic compounds under conditions similar to the primitive atmosphere

Multiple Choice

5. The age of the Earth in billions of years is estimated to be (p. 573)
   a. 2.
   b. 3.
   c. 1.
   d. 4.
   e. 10.

6. The hydrogen of the primordial Earth chemically united with _____ to form methane. (p. 573)
   a. Oxygen
   b. Nitrogen
   c. Carbon
   d. Water

7. The hydrogen of the primordial earth chemically united with _____ to form ammonia. (p. 573)
   a. Oxygen
   b. Nitrogen
   c. Carbon
   d. Phosphorus

8. Which of the following is not an organic compound? (p. 574)
   a. Amino acid
   b. Protein
   c. Water
   d. Methane
   e. Vitamin

9. Which of the following is a eucaryotic cell? (p. 577)
   a. Bacteria
   b. Blue-green algae
   c. Liver cell

10. Which of the following would not be found as fossils in deep Cambrian rocks? (p. 580)
    a. Sponges
    b. Jellyfish
    c. Starfish
    d. Salmon

11. Which of the following have been artificially synthesized? (p. 574)
    a. Amino acids
    b. Vitamins
    c. Monosaccharides
    d. All of these
    e. None of these

12. Which of the following statements best reflects the primitive atmosphere and sea? (p. 573)
    a. The atmosphere and sea both contained large quantities of amino acids.
    b. The atmosphere chemicals mixed and reacted with those in the sea to form a wealth of hydrocarbons.
    c. Atmospheric nitrogen reacted with carbon atoms in the sea to form ammonia.

True—False

13. Sidney Fox, utilizing temperatures of 160-200°C (centigrade), heated a mixture of 18 amino acids and obtained proteinoids. (p. 574)
    a. True   b. False

14. It appears likely that the sea of the primitive Earth spontaneously accumulated a great variety of organic molecules. (p. 575)
    a. True   b. False

15. Organisms that are nutritionally dependent on their environment for ready-made organic substances are called *autotrophs.* (p. 576)
    a. True   b. False

16. The first simple autotroph lived in an aerobic world. (p. 576)
    a. True   b. False

17. The first autotrophs liberated large amounts of carbon dioxide into the atmosphere, thus paving the way for the evolution of photosynthetic cells. (p. 576)
    a. True   b. False

18. Eucaryotic cells contain a well-defined nucleus. (p. 577)
    a. True   b. False

19. The gaseous end product of photosynthesis is oxygen. (p. 576)
    a. True   b. False

20. All bacteria are procaryotic. (p. 577)
    a. True   b. False

21. Fossils provide documentary evidence for the emergence of successively new forms of life. (p. 577)
    a. True   b. False

22. Present-day estimates are that 3 million species of insects exist. (p. 582)
    a. True   b. False

Fill in the Blanks

23. _____ are the remains of organisms preserved or imprinted in the hardened deposits of mud and sand of the earth's crust. (p. 577)

24. The first plants that established themselves on land had leafless stems and were called _____. (p. 579)

25. & 26. In the carboniferous forest the giant club moss was called _____ and the "seed ferns" were called _____. (p. 579)

Matching

27. Archezoic (p. 579)
28. Proterozoic (p. 579)
29. Paleozoic (p. 579)
30. Mesozoic (p. 579)
31. Cenozoic (p. 579)

a. oldest geologic era
b. second geologic era
c. third geologic era
d. fourth geologic era
e. most recent geologic era

True—False

32. In plant history one of the most significant advances was the transition from aquatic existence to life on land. (p. 579)
    a. True   b. False

33. The carboniferous forest existed during the early Mesozoic era. (p. 579)
    a. True   b. False

34. Gymnosperms became prominent in the early Cenozoic era. (p. 579)
    a. True   b. False

35. The deep Cambrian rocks contain the remains of sponges and shellfish. (p. 580)
    a. True   b. False

36. Flowering plants exerted a major influence on the evolution of birds. (p. 582)
    a. True   b. False

VOCABULARY

These are key words or phrases that you should know. By learning these you will achieve learning goal number 22. The page where the respective definition occurs is indicated following the word or phrase.

1. *The Origin of Life* (p. 573)
2. methane (p. 573)
3. ammonia (p. 573)
4. hydrocarbon (p. 573)
5. organic compounds (p. 574)
6. proteinoids (p. 574)
7. microspheres (p. 575)
8. heterotroph (p. 576)
9. autotroph (p. 576)
10. procaryotic (p. 577)
11. eucaryotic (p. 577)
12. fossil (p. 577)
13. geologic eras (p. 579)
14. Psilophytes (p. 579)
15. *Lepidodendron* (p. 579)
16. *Calamite* (p. 579)
17. *Cordaites* (p. 579)
18. *Pteridosperms* (p. 579)
19. angiosperm (p. 579)

STUDY EXERCISES

Instructions: Write out your answers carefully and completely on a separate paper. Check your answers by referring to the text page indicated.

1. Briefly describe the early atmosphere of Earth. (p. 573)
2. Describe how, during the course of evolution, the interaction of plants and animals enhanced the chances of survival of each. (pp. 576-582)
3. How do procaryotic and eucaryotic cells compare and differ? (p. 577)
4. Beginning with the most ancient geologic era list the five main divisions or eras. (p. 579)
5. Discuss the type of plants to be found in the Carboniferous forests. (p. 579)

SELF-POSTTEST OF LEARNING GOALS

Instructions: After completing the vocabulary and study exercises in written form it is now time to review. State each definition orally several times. Reread those areas in your text associated with the study exercises on which you did poorly. Retake the pretest at this time.

ANSWERS

1. a	19. a
2. c	20. a
3. d	21. a
4. b	22. a
5. d	23. fossils
6. c	24. Psilophytes
7. b	25. Lepidodendron
8. c	26. Pteridosperms
9. c	27. a
10. d	28. b
11. d	29. c
12. b	30. d
13. a	31. e
14. a	32. a
15. b	33. b
16. b	34. b
17. a	35. a
18. a	36. a

Chapter 38

Emergence of Man

OVERVIEW

The most advanced Primate is modern man, *Homo sapiens.* Man has many unique characteristics, but he, like all other animals, is the product of many evolutionary changes that began millions of years ago. The Primates, the scientific order to which man belongs, are descendants of a common ancestor. This chapter will present materials that will allow you to follow the evolution of the various forerunners of modern man. Finally, the transition to *Homo sapiens* is completed and comparisons will be made between each genus and species of man. Selected scientific endeavors in the field of evolution are presented, thus allowing you to observe how very recent all theories on the emergence of man are.

LEARNING GOALS

After successfully completing this chapter you should, orally or in writing, be able to do the following.

1. Use appropriately the vocabulary of this chapter when discussing its concepts.
2. State in what geologic era Primates arose.
3. List the members of the modern advanced Primate group.
4. Identify the scientific classification of modern man.
5. State the family to which the ape belongs and the name of the ancestor of today's gibbons.
6. Discuss where Proconsul falls in the evolutionary scheme.
7. Identify the individual who discovered Proconsul.
8. Explain the relationship between *Kenyapithecus* and *Ramapithecus.*
9. State the name of the person(s) who discovered *Kenyapithecus* and *Ramapithecus.*
10. Describe the discovery made in South Africa by Raymond Dart.
11. Explain the meaning of the term *Australopithecus.*
12. Discuss where and by whom *Zinjanthropus* was discovered.
13. Explain the meaning of the term *habilis.*
14. Describe the place in the evolutionary scheme occupied by *Homo habilis.*
15. Discuss the name relationship between *Australopithecus robustus* and *Zinjanthropus,* as well as *Australopithecus africanus* and *Homo habilis.*
16. Describe the coexistence of the two *Australopithecus* species.
17. Discuss the evolution of tools and hunting during the Pleistocene.
18. Describe where and by whom Java man *(Pithecanthropus erectus)* was discovered.
19. Discuss general characteristics of the physical features and accomplishments of Java man.
20. Describe why Java man and Peking man were both classified as *Homo erectus.*
21. Discuss where and by whom Peking man was discovered.
22. Specify the distribution of *Homo erectus* approximately 500,000 years ago.
23. Describe the activities of the *Homo erectus* society.
24. State where Neanderthal man was first discovered, and relate his physical characteristics.
25. Compare brain sizes of each species of the genus *Homo.*
26. Describe how, according to Dobzhansky, the European Neanderthal race and the Middle Eastern modern man contributed to the emergence of Cro-Magnon man.

27. Explain, according to Howell, what effect the glacial ice sheets had on Neanderthalers of western Europe.
28. State where and at what point in time Cro-Magnon man appeared.
29. Describe the over-kill by Cro-Magnon man.
30. Describe the Weidenreich-Coon postulate concerning parallelism.

SELF-PRETEST OF LEARNING GOALS

Before proceeding further in the study of this chapter, attempt to answer the following questions without referring to other information. Upon completion of the test, compare your responses with the answer key at the end of the *Study Guide* chapter. Then correct the wrong responses by referring to the text (page numbers are indicated following each question).

Fill in the Blank

1. Man belongs to the scientific order_____. (p. 587)

2. Primates arose in the_____geologic era. (p. 587)

3.-6. The more advanced primates are the (3)_____, (4) _____, (5)_____, and (6)_____. (p. 587)

7. The scientific classification of modern man is_____. (p. 589)

8. The scientific family to which the ape belongs is_____. (p. 589)

9. _____ is a Miocene gibbonlike creature that is generally regarded as ancestral to today's gibbons. (p. 589)

10. *Proconsul* was discovered by_____. (p. 589)

True—False

11. Louis Leakey discovered *Kenyapithecus.* (p. 591)
    a. True   b. False

12. *Proconsul africanus* followed *Homo erectus* in the evolutionary scheme. (p. 589)
    a. True   b. False

13. *Kenyapithecus* and *Ramapithecus* were discovered by the same scientist. (p. 591)
    a. True   b. False

14. Dart discovered *Australopithecus africanus* in South America. (p. 592)
    a. True   b. False

15. *Australopithecus* means "southern ape." (p. 592)
    a. True   b. False

16. Australopithecines stood upright, walked bipedally and dwelt in open country. (p. 592)
    a. True   b. False

17. *Zinjanthropus* was discovered by Louis and Mary Leakey in east Africa. (pp. 592, 593)
    a. True   b. False

18. *Australopithecus africanus* and *Homo habilis* are one and the same. (p. 594)
    a. True   b. False

19. *Australopithecus robustus* and *Zinjanthropus* are one and the same. (p. 594)
  a. True
  b. False

20. *Habilis* means "able, handy, and vigorous." (p. 593)
  a. True
  b. False

Multiple Choice

21. Which genus and species evolved alongside the Australopithecines? (p. 594)
  a. *Homo erectus*
  b. *Homo habilis*
  c. *Homo mongolis*
  d. *Homo africanus*
  e. *Homo sapiens*

22. Which of the following was the first to fashion tools? (p. 593)
  a. *Homo erectus*
  b. *Homo habilis*
  c. *Homo africanus*
  d. *Homo sapiens*

23. *Pithecanthropus erectus* was first discovered by Dubois in (p. 595)
  a. Africa.
  b. Java.
  c. Australia.
  d. China.
  e. Germany.
  f. Austria.

24. Which of the following best describes Java man? (p. 595)
  a. Low-browed with 770 to 1,000 cc brain and some powers of speech
  b. Six-feet tall with 1,500 cc brain
  c. Four-feet tall with 500 cc brain and nomadic
  d. None of these

25. Who discovered *Sinanthropus pekinensis?* (p. 595)
  a. Reppond
  b. Leakey
  c. Stewell
  d. Cherry
  e. Black
  f. Anderson

26. Why were Peking man and Java man both classified as *Homo erectus?* (pp. 595, 596)
  a. They were not classified as *Homo erectus.*
  b. They were one and the same.
  c. Morphological differences were in the range of variation observed in present living populations.
  d. None of these

27. Which of the following represents the distribution of *Homo sapiens* 500,000 years ago? (pp. 596, 597)
  a. Found only in Asia
  b. Found only in Africa
  c. Found from the tropical regions of Africa to southeast Asia
  d. Found in China and Australia

Matching

28. *Australopithecus* (p. 592)
29. *Homo habilis* (p. 593)
30. Java man (p. 595)
31. modern gorilla (p. 592)
32. Peking man (p. 595)
33. Neanderthal man (p. 597)
34. modern man (p. 597)

  a. brain size of approximately 500 cc
  b. brain size of 900-1,200 cc
  c. brain size of approximately 600 cc
  d. brain size of approximately 680 cc
  e. brain size of 770-1,000 cc
  f. brain size of approximately 1,450 cc
  g. brain size of approximately 1,350 cc

35. Neanderthal man was first unearthed in 1956 near Dusseldorf, Germany, by Raymond Dart. (p. 597)

    a. True   b. False

36. Neanderthal man was a cave dweller, about 5 feet in height, and he first arose some 20,000 years ago. (p. 597)

    a. True   b. False

37. Neanderthal man was replaced by Cro-Magnon man. (p. 597)

    a. True   b. False

38. Prior to the time of Neanderthal man there emerged men, such as Swanscombe and Steinheim, whose skulls are not markedly different from the skull of modern man. (p. 597)

    a. True   b. False

39. Cro-Magnon man, a representative of our own species, *Homo sapiens,* can be traced back about 35,000 years to western and central Europe. (p. 599)

    a. True   b. False

40. Parallelism occurs when two organisms acquire similar characteristics independently of one another. (p. 601)

    a. True   b. False

41. Based on the postulate of Weidenreich and Coon, Peking man was the forerunner of the Negroid race. (p. 601)

    a. True   b. False

42. Cro-Magnon man is believed to have killed off large numbers of animals, some to the point of extinction. (p. 601)

    a. True   b. False

VOCABULARY

These are key words or phrases that you should know. By learning these you will achieve learning goal number 1. The page where the respective definition occurs is indicated following the word or phrase.

1. *Homo sapiens* (p. 589)
2. *Pliopithecus* (p. 589)
3. Pongidae (p. 589)
4. *Proconsul* (p. 589)
5. *Kenyapithecus* (p. 591)
6. *Ramapithecus* (p. 591)
7. *Australopithecus* (p. 592)
8. *Zinjanthropus* (p. 593)
9. *Homo habilis* (p. 593)
10. Java man (p. 594)
11. *Pithecanthropus* (p. 595)
12. Peking man (p. 595)
13. *Homo erectus* (p. 596)
14. Swanscombe man (p. 597)
15. Steinheim man (p. 597)
16. Neanderthal man (p. 597)
17. parallelism (p. 601)
18. divisions of mankind (p. 603)

STUDY EXERCISES

Instructions: Write out your answers carefully and completely on a separate paper. Check your answers by referring to the text page indicated.

1. What was life like in the *Homo erectus* society? (p. 597)
2. What may have caused the abrupt departure of Neanderthal man? (p. 599)

PROBE

1. Where do you place biblical Adam in the scheme of man's evolution?

SELF-POSTTEST OF LEARNING GOALS

Instructions: After completing the vocabulary and study exercises in written form it is now time to review. State each definition orally several times. Reread those areas in your text associated with the study exercises on which you did poorly. Retake the pretest at this time.

ANSWERS

1. Primate	22. b
2. Cenozoic	23. b
3. New World monkey	24. a
4. Old World monkey	25. e
5. apes	26. c
6. man	27. c
7. *Homo sapiens*	28. c
8. *Pongidae*	29. d
9. *Pliopithecus*	30. e
10. Louis Leakey	31. a
11. a	32. b
12. b	33. f
13. b	34. g
14. b	35. b
15. a	36. b
16. a	37. a
17. a	38. a
18. a	39. a
19. a	40. a
20. a	41. b
21. b	42. a

Chapter 39

Population Dynamics

OVERVIEW

One major characteristic of all life is the ability to reproduce, for without this ability no species can be maintained. If all offspring were to survive, this planet would literally be overrun within a few generations. The survival of offspring is regulated by disease, famine, predators, and territoriality. All organisms, including man, are required to live within the system of checks and balances in nature. Population dynamics will be discussed at length with emphasis placed on human population growth.

LEARNING GOALS

After successfully completing this chapter you should, orally or in writing, be able to do the following.

1. Use appropriately the vocabulary associated with this chapter when discussing its concepts.
2. Describe a species population.
3. Explain the growth pattern of simple asexually reproducing organisms as observed by Gause under controlled experimental conditions.
4. Discuss environmental resistance.
5. Cite general causes of population fluctuations.
6. Name the self-regulating factors affecting population.
7. Explain the density effect on population.
8. Describe the social stress experimentation of Dennis Chitty.
9. Discuss the possible relationship between stress and physiological feedback.
10. State the relationship between selection and reproductive fitness.
11. Explain differential dispersal.
12. State the human population prediction of Raymond Pearl in 1921.
13. Explain human volition.
14. Designate the three main categories of population as stated by Bodenheimer.
15. Describe how the age pyramids for the United States changed between 1900 and 1958.
16. Show how the birth rate is expressed.
17. Explain how the fertility rate is determined.
18. Cite the age ranges of the highly fertile female.
19. Give the predicted population increase in the United States by the year 2000.
20. Cite the trend in the United States for both birth rate and fertility rate.

SELF-PRETEST OF LEARNING GOALS

Before proceeding further in the study of this chapter, attempt to answer the following questions without referring to other information. Upon completion of the test, compare your responses with the answer key at the end of the *Study Guide* chapter. Then correct the wrong responses by referring to the text (page numbers are indicated following each question).

Fill in the Blank

1. The word _____ is derived from the Latin *populus,* meaning "people." (p. 609)

2. A _____ population is a local breeding unit in which the constituent individuals are capable of exchanging genes with each other. (p. 609)

3. _____ is a term denoting the production of new-generation offspring. (p. 609)

4. Under controlled experimental conditions, particularly with simple asexually reproducing organisms, the growth pattern of a population is _____ shaped. (p. 609)

5. The eventual restraint on the innate growth capacity of the population by some force in the environment is termed _____. (p. 611)

6. The limit at which the environment can support a population is often referred to as the _____ capacity of the environment. (p. 611)

True—False

7. Natural populations generally do not remain perfectly steady around an asymptote. (p. 611)
   a. True
   b. False

8. The main external forces that keep the density of populations within certain limits are starvation, predators, parasites, and disease. (p. 611)
   a. True
   b. False

9. Self-regulating factors that affect population are starvation and sterility. (p. 615)
   a. True
   b. False

10. High population densities have adverse effects on the longevity and fecundity of the individuals. (p. 615)
    a. True
    b. False

11. Crowding causes the frequency of copulation to increase. (p. 615)
    a. True
    b. False

12. Canadian ecologist Dennis Chitty stated that a high population density leads to physiological derangement among the adults, resulting in low fetal mortality. (p. 618)
    a. True
    b. False

Multiple Choice

13. Which of the following animal organs, according to Christian, are involved in the relationship between stress and physiological feedback? (p. 618)
    a. Pituitary gland
    b. Adrenal gland
    c. Pancreas
    d. All of these
    e. All but one of these
    f. None of these

14. According to Christian, the oversecretion of which of the following hormones leads to severe physiological stress? (p. 618)
    a. Pitocin
    b. Thyroxine
    c. Cortisone
    d. Insulin
    e. Estrogen
    f. None of these

15. When individuals who are genetically superior migrate and leave behind the inferior members of the population, we observe (p. 619)
    a. innate movement.
    b. territorial regression.
    c. differential dispersal.
    d. loci dependability.

16. When an individual gains possession of a certain area and excludes other members of the same sex and species, and sometimes all species members except a mate, we observe (p. 619)
    a. innate control.
    b. differential dispersal.
    c. territoriality.
    d. loci dependability.

17. Raymond Pearl, in 1921, predicted that the human population would stabilize in 2100 A.D. at _____billion. (pp. 619, 620)
    a. 1.5
    b. 2.0
    c. 2.6
    d. 5.0
    e. 10.0
    f. 7.5

18. The current world population is approximately_____billion. (p. 620)
    a. 2.5
    b. 1.8
    c. 4.0
    d. 8.0
    e. 9.2
    f. 6.0

True—False

19. The evidence suggests that a decline in the human birth rate is due almost wholly to human volition. (p. 620)
    a. True
    b. False

20. One of the most fundamental features of any population is that fertility and mortality are not age-related. (p. 620)
    a. True
    b. False

21. In rapidly expanding populations, it is primarily the declining death rate, instead of an increasing birth rate, that brings about a population explosion. (p. 620)
    a. True
    b. False

22. In the United States, 15 years were added to the average life expectancy between 1900 and 1940. (p. 622)
    a. True
    b. False

23. The proportion of people in the United States 65 years of age and over continues to increase. (p. 622)
    a. True
    b. False

24. Between 1900 and 1958 in the United States the population increased most at the two extremes, the young and the old. (p. 622)
    a. True
    b. False

25. The birth rate is expressed as births per 1,000 individuals of a population. (p. 623)
    a. True
    b. False

26. The fertility rate is the annual number of live births per 1,000 women in the population. (p. 623)
    a. True
    b. False

27. The highly fertile females are between the ages of 15 and 35 years of age. (p. 624)
    a. True
    b. False

28. The most conservative projection indicates a population increase of nearly 100 million people in the United States by the year 2000. (p. 624)
    a. True   b. False

29. The birth rate is declining while the fertility rate is increasing in the United States. (p. 624)
    a. True   b. False

VOCABULARY

These are key words or phrases that you should know. By learning these you will achieve learning goal number 1. The page where the respective definition occurs is indicated following the word or phrase.

1. population (p. 609)
2. species population (p. 609)
3. natality (p. 609)
4. mortality (p. 609)
5. logistic curve (p. 609)
6. environmental resistance (p. 611)
7. carrying capacity (p. 611)
8. self-regulating factors (p. 615)
9. differential dispersal (p. 619)
10. territoriality (p. 619)
11. human volition (p. 620)
12. birth rate (p. 623)
13. fertility rate (p. 623)
14. highly fertile female (p. 624)
15. density (p. 609)

STUDY EXERCISES

Instructions: Write out your answers carefully and completely on a separate paper. Check your answers by referring to the textbook page indicated.

1. Describe the logistic theory of population growth. (p. 609)
2. How has the composition of persons in population age groups changed in percentages since 1900? (pp. 621, 622)
3. Describe the population predictions in the United States for the year 2000 concerning the total population and for the highly fertile female group. (pp. 620, 624)

SELF-POSTTEST OF LEARNING GOALS

Instructions: After completing the vocabulary and study exercises in written form it is now time to review. State each definition orally several times. Reread those areas in your text associated with the study exercises on which you did poorly. Retake the pretest at this time.

ANSWERS

1. population	11. b	21. a
2. species	12. b	22. a
3. Natality	13. e	23. a
4. S	14. c	24. a
5. environmental resistance	15. c	25. a
6. carrying	16. c	26. b
7. a	17. c	27. b
8. a	18. c	28. a
9. b	19. a	29. b
10. a	20. b	

Chapter 40

Interactions of Populations

OVERVIEW

In any given community numerous populations of various plant and animal species exist together. This interaction is necessary, for animals and plants are dependent on each other for survival. Many times two populations of different species in the community compete and only one survives. Other times competition will result in the reduction of one species but not total elimination. In this chapter the interaction of populations will be presented with emphasis on the result of competition.

LEARNING GOALS

After successfully completing this chapter you should, orally or in writing, be able to do the following.

1. Use appropriately the vocabulary associated with this chapter when discussing its concepts.
2. Explain Gause's principle of coexistence.
3. State the result when two species populations are competing for precisely the same limited resource.
4. Cite the findings of Crombie as they relate to competition between two species populations.
5. State how many species of wildlife in the United States were listed in 1971 as being in danger of becoming extinct.
6. Explain the relationships of predator and prey.
7. Describe the three kinds of symbiotic relationships.
8. Discuss the life cycle of *Plasmodium.*
9. Cite four different types of flatworms.
10. State the effect of building the Aswan High Dam on the incidence of schistosomiasis in Egypt.
11. Relate how schistosomiasis is transmitted.

SELF-PRETEST OF LEARNING GOALS

Before proceeding further in the study of this chapter, attempt to answer the following questions without referring to other information. Upon completion of the test, compare your responses with the answer key at the end of the *Study Guide* chapter. Then correct the wrong responses by referring to the text (page numbers are indicated following each question).

Fill in the Blank

1. Competitive exclusion is also known as_____principle. (p. 629)

2. _____may be defined as the interaction of species populations that utilize a limited resource in an environment common to them. (p. 629)

3. The sum total of environmental requirements for a species to thrive and reproduce has been termed the_____of that species population. (p. 631)

4. When members of two different species are capable of living together the condition is termed _____. (p. 636)

5. Malaria in man is caused by protozoans that belong to the genus_____. (p. 640)

True—False

6. Gause's principle states that no two species with identical requirements can continue to exist together. (p. 631)
   a. True   b. False

7. Combie (1945) demonstrated that even in laboratory cultures, two species can live together indefinitely if they differ even slightly in their food requirements. (p. 630)
   a. True   b. False

8. Competition between two species populations achieves the avoidance or reduction of further competition, not an intensification. (p. 632)
   a. True   b. False

9. When the prey population increases the numbers of predators decrease. (p. 635)
   a. True   b. False

10. An increase in predators decreases the prey population. (p. 635)
    a. True   b. False

11. The predator-prey interaction generally results in a cyclic pattern. (p. 635)
    a. True   b. False

12. A classic example of mutualism is the lichen. (p. 638)
    a. True   b. False

Matching

13. Commensalism (p. 637)
14. Mutualism (p. 638)
15. Parasitism (p. 638)

a. one species benefits from symbiosis, other species is not benefited or adversely affected
b. close relationship in which both species benefit
c. symbiosis wherein one species actually eats at the expense of the other

Matching

16. Commensalism (p. 637)
17. Mutualism (p. 638)
18. Parasitism (p. 638)

a. lichen
b. liver fluke
c. Spanish moss
d. none of these

Matching

19. Tapeworm (p. 642)
20. Liver fluke (p. 642)
21. Lung fluke (p. 642)
22. Blood fluke (p. 642)

a. flatworm
b. roundworm
c. segmented worm
d. marine worm
e. none of these

True—False

23. The female mosquito that harbors the sexual phase of *Plasmodium* belongs to the *Anopheles* genus. (p. 640)
    a. True   b. False

24. Human schistosomiasis has as an essential intermediate host the grasshopper. (p. 642)
    a. True   b. False

25. As a consequence of building the Aswan High Dam in Egypt, it is estimated that 80 percent of the Egyptian population suffers from schistosomiasis. (p. 643)
    a. True   b. False

26. In the United States approximately 100 species of wildlife were listed in 1971 as being in danger of becoming extinct. (p. 633)
    a. True   b. False

VOCABULARY

These are key words or phrases that you should know. By learning these you will achieve learning goal number 1. The page where the respective definition occurs is indicated following the word or phrase.

1. Gause's principle (p. 629)
2. niche (p. 631)
3. symbiosis (p. 636)
4. commensalism (p. 637)
5. epiphyte (p. 637)
6. mutualism (p. 638)
7. lichen (p. 638)
8. parasitism (p. 638)
9. *Plasmodium* (p. 640)
10. *Anopheles* (p. 640)
11. vector-borne (p. 641)
12. trypanosomiasis (p. 641)
13. schistosomiasis (p. 642)

STUDY EXERCISES

Instructions: Write out your answers carefully and completely on separate paper. Check your answers by referring to the text page indicated.

1. Describe Gause's principle of competitive exclusion. (pp. 629-631)
2. Differentiate between the various types of symbiosis. (pp. 636-638)
3. Explain the life cycle of the organism that causes malaria. (pp. 640, 641)
4. Briefly describe how the construction of the Aswan High Dam changed the incidence of schistosomiasis among the Egyptian population. (p. 643)

SELF-POSTTEST OF LEARNING GOALS

Instructions: After completing the vocabulary and study exercises in written form it is now time to review. State each definition orally several times. Reread those areas in your text associated with the study exercises on which you did poorly. Retake the pretest at this time.

ANSWERS

1. Gause's	14. b
2. Competition	15. c
3. niche	16. c
4. symbiosis	17. a
5. *Plasmodium*	18. b
6. a	19. a
7. a	20. a
8. a	21. a
9. b	22. a
10. a	23. a
11. a	24. b
12. a	25. a
13. a	26. a

Chapter 41

Biotic Communities

OVERVIEW

One characteristic of every biotic community is the need for a supply of energy. This supply is derived from the nutrients available to the various organisms of the biotic community. Each community has its own physical structure as well as a unique group of plants and animals. It is the interaction of these plants and animals that allows the community to maintain a stability. In this chapter the significance of the food chain will be emphasized.

LEARNING GOALS

After successfully completing this chapter you should, orally or in writing, be able to do the following.

1. Describe a food chain.
2. State the function of the chlorophyll molecule in photosynthesis.
3. Use appropriately the vocabulary associated with this chapter when discussing its concepts.
4. Write the general overall chemical equation for the process of photosynthesis.
5. Discuss the two main stages of photosynthesis, the light reaction and the dark reaction.
6. Describe how Calvin and his associates were able to identify many of the steps in the process of photosynthesis.
7. State what relation exists between the rate of photosynthesis and the concentration of carbon dioxide in the atmosphere.
8. Cite the effect of man's extensive combustion of fossils fuels on the concentration of atmospheric carbon dioxide.
9. Name examples of fossil fuels.
10. Describe the *greenhouse effect*.
11. State what percent of the world's photosynthetic activity is attributed to phytoplankton.
12. Cite the role of the green plant in the food chain.
13. Differentiate between primary and secondary consumers.
14. Differentiate between herbivores, omnivores, and carnivores.
15. Describe a food web.
16. State the first and second laws of thermodynamics.
17. Discuss how the energy flow occurs in a biotic community.
18. Cite the fate of solar radiation reaching the surface of the earth.
19. Explain why an oversimplified food chain is greatly susceptible to an ecologic catastrophe.

SELF-PRETEST OF LEARNING GOALS

Before proceeding further in the study of this chapter, attempt to answer the following questions without referring to other information. Upon completion of the test, compare your responses with the answer key at the end of the *Study Guide* chapter. Then correct the wrong responses by referring to the text (page numbers are indicated following each question).

Fill in the Blank

1. A_____ is an organized association of different, interacting species. (p. 647)

2. The sequence of organisms through which energy is channeled is called_____

   _____(p. 647)

3. _____is the process by which the energy of sunlight is used in the conversion of carbon dioxide and water into glucose and free oxygen. (p. 647)

4. The green pigment in plants is_____. (p. 647)

5. The synthesis of glucose involves the transfer of hydrogen to carbon dioxide, using the energy of

   _____. (p. 649)

Multiple Choice

6. Which molecule has the function of absorbing light energy? (p. 647)
   - a. Glucose
   - b. ATP
   - c. Chlorophyll
   - d. Sucrose
   - e. Water
   - f. Carbon dioxide

7. Which of the following represents the correct simplified overall equation for photosynthesis? (p. 647)
   - a. $6CO_2 + 6H_2O$ + absorbed light energy $\rightarrow C_{12}H_{22}O_{11} + 6O_2$ + chemical energy
   - b. $3CO_2 + 9H_2O$ + light $\rightarrow C_6H_{12}O_6 + H_2O$
   - c. $6CO_2 + 6H_2O$ + light $\rightarrow 3C_6H_{12}O_6 + O_2 + H_2O$
   - d. $6CO_2 + 6H_2O$ + absorbed light energy $\rightarrow C_6H_{12}O_6 + 6O_2$ + chemical energy

8. Photosynthesis has (p. 647)
   - a. two stages: light reaction and dark reaction.
   - b. two stages: light reaction and glucose activation.
   - c. three stages: light reaction, glucose activation, and water release.
   - d. none of these.

9. Which of the following is a hydrogen carrier? (p. 647)
   - a. ATP
   - b. Glucose
   - c. NADP
   - d. Chlorophyll
   - e. Carbon dioxide

10. Which of the following constitutes the first level of the food chain? (p. 647)
    - a. Animals (plant-eaters)
    - b. Animals (meat-eaters)
    - c. Single-celled organisms
    - d. Photosynthetic green plants
    - e. Bacteria

11. Which individual received the Nobel prize (1961) in chemistry for his identification of the intermediate steps through which carbon passes from carbon dioxide to carbohydrates? (p. 649)
    - a. Krebs
    - b. Reppond
    - c. Hughensin
    - d. Calvin
    - e. Campbell

12. Which of the following is/are fossil fuels? (p. 649)
    - a. Coal
    - b. Natural gas
    - c. Oil
    - d. All of these
    - e. None of these

Matching

13. Herbivores (p. 651)   a. plant-eaters
14. Carnivores (p. 651)   b. meat-eaters and plant-eaters
15. Omnivores (p. 651)   c. meat-eaters

Matching

16. First law of thermodynamics (p. 653)   a. energy on earth is neither created nor de-
17. Second law of thermodynamics (p. 653)   stroyed
                                            b. at each energy transformation a certain propor-
                                                tion of the available energy is dissipated as heat

True—False

18. The first trophic level of a food chain is represented by the producers. (p. 650)
    a.   True   b.   False

19. Animals that feed directly on plants are primary consumers. (p. 650)
    a.   True   b.   False

20. All secondary consumers are herbivores. (p. 650)
    a.   True   b.   False

21. Bacteria and fungi may serve as decomposers in the food chain. (p. 651)
    a.   True   b.   False

22. In a biotic community, numerous food chains are interwoven in a complex food web. (p. 652)
    a.   True   b.   False

23. Organisms at successively higher tropic levels pass onto others less energy than they receive.
    (p. 653)
    a.   True   b.   False

24. Most of the solar radiation reaching the surface of the earth is absorbed or reflected into space.
    (p. 653)
    a.   True   b.   False

25. The biomass is the total amount of living matter in a community. (p. 654)
    a.   True   b.   False

26. Phytoplankton account for 40-60% of the world's photosynthetic activity. (p. 650)
    a.   True   b.   False

27. As atmospheric carbon dioxide increases the earth's temperature decreases. (pp. 649, 650)
    a.   True   b.   False

28. The carbon dioxide level of the atmosphere has decreased over the past 100 years. (p. 649)
    a.   True   b.   False

29. An oversimplified food chain can easily be affected by an ecologic catastrophe. (p. 656)
    a.   True   b.   False

VOCABULARY

These are key words or phrases that you should know. By learning these you will achieve learning goal number 3. The page where the respective definition occurs is indicated following the word or phrase.

1. biotic community (p. 647)
2. food chain (p. 647)
3. chlorophyll (p. 647)
4. photosynthesis (p. 647)
5. NADP (p. 647)
6. light and dark reactions (p. 647)
7. fossil fuels (p. 649)
8. greenhouse effect (pp. 649, 650)
9. phytoplankton (p. 650)
10. producer (p. 650)
11. consumer (p. 650)
12. herbivore (p. 651)
13. carnivore (p. 651)
14. omnivore (p. 651)
15. decomposer (p. 651)
16. food web (p. 652)
17. first law of thermodynamics (p. 653)
18. second law of thermodynamics (p. 653)
19. biomass (p. 654)

STUDY EXERCISES

Instructions: Write out your answers carefully and completely on a separate paper. Check your answers by referring to the text page indicated.

1. Explain the position of man in the food chain. (pp. 655, 656)
2. Describe the light and dark reactions of photosynthesis. (pp. 647, 649)
3. What relation exists between primary and secondary consumers? (p. 650)
4. Why would oversimplification of a food chain make it especially susceptible to an ecologic catastrophe? (pp. 656, 657)

SELF-POSTTEST OF LEARNING GOALS

Instructions: After completing the vocabulary and study exercises in written form it is now time to review. State each definition orally several times. Reread those areas in your text associated with the study exercises on which you did poorly. Retake the pretest at this time.

ANSWERS

1. community
2. food chain
3. photosynthesis
4. chlorophyll
5. ATP
6. c
7. d
8. a
9. c
10. d
11. d
12. d
13. a
14. c
15. b
16. a
17. b
18. a
19. a
20. b
21. a
22. a
23. a
24. a
25. a
26. a
27. b
28. b
29. a

Chapter 42

The Ecosystem

OVERVIEW

An ecosystem consists of all the living (biotic) and the nonliving (chemicophysical) components. It is important that one remembers that plants depend on animals and vice versa. What has not been emphasized is that the nonliving physical and chemical portions play equally important roles in the balance of nature. For thousands of years the various ecosystems of the world operated in harmony. The system of checks and balances in nature produced a peaceful unity between living and nonliving materials. Then, only recently, a new animal called *man* began to exert a dominant influence over all ecosystems. His wants and desires came first and many unnecessary pressures were exerted on various ecosystems. Change in all ecosystems is now being observed. This chapter will explain how an ideal ecosystem functions and emphasizes how man has pressured the ecosystems on the planet Earth.

LEARNING GOALS

After successfully completing this chapter you should, orally or in writing, be able to do the following.

1. Use appropriately the vocabulary associated with this chapter when discussing its concepts.
2. Describe an ecosystem.
3. Differentiate between autotrophic and heterotrophic.
4. Explain saprophytic nutrition.
5. Cite examples of abiotic substances.
6. State how many chemical elements occur in nature.
7. Cite how many elements are required by living organisms and which are of paramount importance.
8. Explain the carbon cycle.
9. State what percentage of the earth's carbon actually circulates in the atmosphere.
10. Cite how and at what rate the atmospheric carbon dioxide concentration has changed since 1958.
11. Describe some of the long-term consequences of anticipated increases in atmospheric carbon dioxide.
12. State how much fossil fuel is now burned in the United States and what percent of the world's consumption this represents.
13. Discuss the nitrogen cycle and relate the role of nitrogen-fixing and denitrifying bacteria to the cycle.
14. Explain the process of ammonification and relate it to nitrification.
15. Relate the role of sulfur and phosphorus in the ecosystem.
16. State how many tons of sulfur are released annually into the atmosphere by companies in the United States as a result of burning fossil fuels.
17. Explain how phosphorus is made available to plants.
18. Cite the effect of the annual increase in the use of phosphate fertilizers on the known supply and reserves in the world.
19. Describe homeostasis in an ecosystem.
20. Discuss how the congregation of man into towns and cities has affected the ecosystem.

21. Relate the effect of man on the aging of Lake Erie.
22. State what the human population was in the late 1700s and what it is at present along the shores of Lake Erie.
23. Explain the ecological effects of the tremendous population growth and industrialization around Lake Erie.
24. Describe the effect of dumping large quantities of raw sewage into an aquatic ecosystem.
25. State the significance of a high biochemical oxygen demand (BOD).
26. Cite the sources of oxygen in lake water.
27. Relate the effect of the two phases of sewage waste treatment on the general growth pattern of algae.
28. Explain eutrophication.
29. Describe the effect of excessive alga mortality on the level of dissolved oxygen in lake water.
30. Cite the major consideration when attempting to save a lake.

SELF-PRETEST OF LEARNING GOALS

Before proceeding further in the study of this chapter, attempt to answer the following questions without referring to other information. Upon completion of the test, compare your responses with the answer key at the end of the *Study Guide* chapter. Then correct the wrong responses by referring to the text (page numbers are indicated following each question).

Fill in the Blank

1. The _____ is a self-contained unit characterized by an orderly flow of energy and materials between the organisms and their environment. (p. 661)

2. Plants are termed _____ (self-nourishing) because they can trap light energy and manufacture their own food. (p. 661)

3. Organisms that lack the ability to manufacture their own organic nutrients are termed _____ (other-nourishing). (p. 661)

4. The organisms of decay are decomposers, the bacteria and fungi; their nutrition is termed _____ (rotten). (p. 661)

5. Chemicals in an ecosystem flow continually between the organisms and the environment in circular pathways that are known as _____ cycles. (p. 663)

6. Approximately _____ elements of the chemist's periodic table occur in nature. (p. 663)

7. About _____ elements are known to be required by living organisms. (p. 663)

8. Carbon exists in the atmosphere primarily as gaseous _____. (p. 663)

9. The total world ocean contains approximately _____ times as much CO_2 as the atmosphere. (p. 663)

10.-12. Most of the carbon in the earth's crust exists as organic fossil deposits, chiefly _____, _____, and _____. (p. 663)

13.-14. In the United States alone, the equivalent of _____ billion tons of fossil fuels is now burned each year, representing _____ percent of the world's consumption. (p. 663)

15. The prediction is that the amount of CO_2 in the atmosphere will rise from its present value of 330 ppm to _____ ppm by the year 2000. (p. 663)

True—False

16. Sir Arthur George Tansley (1935) proposed the term *ecosystem*. (p. 661)
    a. True   b. False

17. Carbon, nitrogen, and oxygen are abiotic substances. (pp. 661, 663)
    a. True   b. False

18. Fungi are autotrophic. (p. 661)
    a. True   b. False

19. The atmospheric CO_2 concentration has been steadily decreasing since 1958. (p. 663)
    a. True   b. False

20. Smoke, dust, and particulate matter in the atmosphere increases the atmosphere's reflectivity for solar radiation. (p. 664)
    a. True   b. False

21. Through death and bacterial action, the nitrogenous compounds of plants and animals are decomposed, or converted to ammonium ions, by a process known as *denitrification*. (p. 665)
    a. True   b. False

22. The series of reactions by which the ammonium ion is transformed to nitrate is termed *ammonification*. (p. 665)
    a. True   b. False

23. The nitrite ion is symbolized as NO_2^-. (p. 665)
    a. True   b. False

24. Calcium nitrate is an example of a soluble nitrate. (p. 665)
    a. True   b. False

25. Sulfur is an important constituent of all amino acids. (p. 667)
    a. True   b. False

26. The sulfur-containing proteins in plants and animals are degraded to hydrogen sulfide by a variety of soil bacteria. (p. 667)
    a. True   b. False

27. Approximately 6 million tons of sulfur are released annually into the atmosphere by the industrial burning of fossil fuels in the United States. (p. 667)
    a. True   b. False

Multiple Choice

28. Which of the following is/are amino acids? (p. 667)
    a. methionine   c. phosphorus
    b. glucose   d. ammonia

29. Other than nitrogen and sulfur, which of the following is made available to plants through the action of soil bacteria? (p. 667)
    a. methionine   d. calcium
    b. phosphorus   e. sucrose
    c. ammonia

30. Which of the following are air pollutants? (pp. 665, 667)
    a. Nitrogen dioxide   c. Both of these
    b. Sulfur dioxide   d. Neither of these

31. Concern has been voiced that if world population grows at an annual rate of 2 percent, and if the use of phosphate fertilizers continues to increase, known supply and reserves of phosporus will be gone in_____years. (p. 667)
    a. 9   d. 90
    b. 900   e. 25
    c. 10,000   f. 1,600

32. The population around Lake Erie in the late 1700s was approximately _____. (p. 670)
    a. 1,000,000   c. 10,000
    b. 10,000,000   d. 100,000

33. At present, the population along the shores of Lake Erie is _____. (p. 670)
    a. 1,300,000   d. 13,000
    b. 130,000   e. 130,000,000
    c. 13,000,000

34. The natural process of the accumulation of nutrients and aging of a lake is termed _____.
    (p. 670)
    a. eutrophication   c. oligotrophication
    b. ammonification   d. mesotrophication

True—False

35. More than one-third of America's 100,000 lakes now show signs of unnatural stress as direct or indirect consequences of man's activities. (p. 669)
    a. True   b. False

36. Homeostasis is the delicate balance that exists in an ecosystem. (p. 668)
    a. True   b. False

37. When large quantities of untreated sewage are added to an aquatic ecosystem, the biogeochemical cycle is stressed. (p. 670)
    a. True   b. False

38. A high biochemical oxygen demand (BOD) value indicates large amounts of degradable organic materials. (p. 670)
    a. True   b. False

39. Oxygen in lake water comes only from photosynthesis by plants in the water. (p. 670)
    a. True   b. False

40. In normal sewage treatment, the secondary step is designed to degrade organic materials. (p. 671)
    a. True   b. False

41. After sewage treatment the effluent is richer in phosphates than in nitrates. (p. 671)
    a. True   b. False

42. Phosphates and nitrates from sewage effluent enhance algae growth. (p. 671)
    a. True   b. False

43. Greater use of phosphate-containing detergents has increased algae growth in lakes. (p. 671)
    a. True   b. False

44. Increased algae death decreases oxygen dissolved in lake water. (p. 671)
   a. True   b. False

45. To save a lake, the paramount consideration is the management of phosphate. (p. 672)
   a. True   b. False

VOCABULARY

These are key words or phrases that you should know. By learning these you will achieve learning goal number 1. The page where the respective definition occurs is indicated following the word or phrase.

1. ecosystem (p. 661)
2. autotrophic (p. 661)
3. heterotrophic (p. 661)
4. saprophytic (p. 661)
5. abiotic substances (p. 661)
6. biogeochemical cycles (p. 663)
7. carbon cycle (p. 663)
8. nitrogen-fixing bacteria (p. 665)
9. denitrifying bacteria (p. 665)
10. ammonification (p. 665)
11. ammonifying bacteria (p. 665)
12. nitrification (p. 665)
13. homeostasis (p. 668)
14. Lake Erie (pp. 669, 670)
15. eutrophication (p. 670)
16. oligotrophic (p. 670)
17. mesotrophic (p. 670)
18. biochemical oxygen demand (p. 670)
19. sewage treatment (p. 671)
20. zooplankton (p. 671)

STUDY EXERCISES

Instructions: Write out your answers carefully and completely on a separate paper. Check your answers by referring to the text page indicated.

1. Differentiate between autotrophic, heterotrophic, and saprophytic. (p. 661)
2. Describe the main features of the carbon cycle. (p. 663)
3. What is the probable consequence of increases in atmospheric CO_2? (pp. 663, 664)
4. Describe the role of denitrifying bacteria in the nitrogen cycle. (p. 665)
5. Explain the consequences of increased algae growth on a freshwater lake. (pp. 670, 671)

SELF-POSTTEST OF LEARNING GOALS

Instructions: After completing the vocabulary and study exercises in written form it is now time to review. State each definition orally several times. Reread those areas in your text associated with the study exercises on which you did poorly. Retake the pretest at this time.

ANSWERS

1. ecosystem	13. 1.9	24. a	35. a
2. autotrophic	14. 30	25. b	36. a
3. heterotrophic	15. 400	26. a	37. a
4. saprophytic	16. a	27. a	38. a
5. biogeochemical	17. a	28. a	39. b
6. 92	18. b	29. b	40. a
7. 40	19. b	30. c	41. a
8. carbon dioxide	20. a	31. d	42. a
9. 60	21. b	32. c	43. a
10. oil shale	22. b	33. c	44. a
11. coal	23. a	34. a	45. a
12. petroleum			

Chapter 43

Man's Modification of the Environment

OVERVIEW

As the population of man on this planet continues to increase, advances in technology allow this massive population to literally disrupt natural ecosystems that have been in balance for tens of thousands of years. Man has, in just over 50 years, polluted this planet so extensively that recent predictions indicate that it would be necessary for all mankind not to pollute for 100 years just to allow us to return to the environmental level of 1960. Man is using up raw materials, ignoring recycling, and dumping toxic waste into the air, water, and soil. Naturally, as the population grows the pollution problem intensifies.

Many less advanced countries yearn to be industrialized like the United States. With increased foreign aid, these over-populated countries are realizing their dream and we are observing another reason for the increasing planetary pollution problem. All of mankind must realize that the preservation of the environment is the preservation of man. Without man working to be a part of the natural ecosystem, he will not only destroy himself but many other plant and animal species. In this chapter we will observe how man has modified the environment and how all mankind can contribute to a reduction in degradation to the environment.

LEARNING GOALS

After successfully completing this chapter you should, orally or in writing, be able to do the following.

1. Use appropriately the vocabulary associated with this chapter when discussing its concepts.
2. Describe the composition of the thin envelope of air that surrounds the earth.
3. List the sources and examples of air pollutants.
4. Describe the components of smog.
5. Explain how sulfuric acid could be formed as a by-product of air pollution.
6. Cite the major cause of air pollution in the United States.
7. Compare the level of pollutants released by various types of engines.
8. State the one serious drawback of nuclear energy.
9. List examples of the hazardous and long-lived radioisotopes produced as waste by present-day nuclear power plants.
10. Cite the tissues in which strontium 90 and cesium 137 tend to accumulate.
11. State the principal hazard to man from strontium 90.
12. Explain how and why Eskimos have absorbed more radioactive cesium than the general population.
13. Cite the effect of agricultural fertilizers and modern detergents on the rate of lake aging.
14. List industrial wastes that are classed as poisons.
15. Discuss the physiological effect of high levels of mercury.
16. Cite the estimate by Dr. Blumer of how much oil is poured into the oceans each year.
17. Give the name of the chemist who first synthesized DDT.
18. Relate the rate at which DDT is biograded.

157

19. Cite the approximate amount of DDT currently circulating in the biosphere.
20. Discuss the physiological effects of DDT.
21. Give the name of the author of *Silent Spring*.
22. List examples of chlorinated hydrocarbons.

SELF-PRETEST OF LEARNING GOALS

Before proceeding further in the study of this chapter, attempt to answer the following questions without referring to other information. Upon completion of the test, compare your responses with the answer key at the end of the *Study Guide* chapter. Then correct the wrong responses by referring to the text (page numbers are indicated following each question).

Matching

Composition of air (p. 678)

1. Nitrogen	a. 78 percent
2. Oxygen	b. 1 percent
3. Other gases	c. 21 percent

Matching

Pollutants and their sources (p. 678)

4. Steel mill	a. hydrocarbons
5. Paint factory	b. carbon monoxide
6. Auto exhaust	c. SO_2

True—False

7. Smog contains, among other things, hydrocarbons, carbon monoxide, nitrous oxide, soot, and dust. (p. 678)

    a. True   b. False

8. Smog may contribute to, or precipitate, such diseases as bronchitis, emphysema, and asthma. (pp. 678, 680)

    a. True   b. False

9. When burned, soft coal releases carbon dioxide, which combines with moisture in the air to form sulfuric acid. (p. 680)

    a. True   b. False

10. Comparatively little sulfur dioxide originates from the operation of gasoline-burning internal combustion engines. (p. 680)

    a. True   b. False

11. Diesel and steam engines release more carbon monoxide than the gasoline-burning internal combustion engine. (p. 680)

    a. True   b. False

Multiple Choice

12. Which of the following produce the largest percentage of the air pollution in the United States? (p. 680)

a. Automobile exhausts	c. Sewage plants
b. Steel mills	d. Diesel trains

13. Which of the following represents the serious drawback of producing nuclear energy? (p. 682)
    a. Large quantity of water needed to cool core
    b. Large space needed for installation
    c. Expense too high for nuclear source
    d. Production of large quantities of radioactive wastes

14. Which of the following are radioisotopes? (p. 682)
    a. Strontium 90   d. None of these
    b. Iodine 131   e. All of these
    c. Cesium 137

15. Strontium 90 tends to accumulate in (p. 682)
    a. bone.   c. thyroid.
    b. muscle.   d. brain.

16. Iodine 131 tends to accumulate in (p. 682)
    a. bone.   c. thyroid.
    b. muscle.   d. brain.

17. Which of the following represent the reason(s) that Eskimos have absorbed more radioactive cesium than most people in the world? (p. 682)
    a. They consume large quantities of beef contaminated with cesium.
    b. They eat caribou that have eaten lichens that have collected cesium from the atmosphere.
    c. Both of the above
    d. None of the above

18. The principal hazard to man from strontium 90 is (p. 682)
    a. thyroid enlargement.   c. leukemia.
    b. atrophy of testes and ovaries.   d. atherosclerosis.

True—False

19. Man has hastened the aging of lakes through the use of agricultural fertilizers and modern detergents. (p. 683)
    a. True   b. False

20. Lead, arsenic, and mercury are classed as industrial poisons. (p. 683)
    a. True   b. False

21. Dr. Max Blumer estimates that at least 10 million tons of oil are poured into the oceans annually. (p. 683)
    a. True   b. False

22. Mercury collects in nervous tissue of mammals. (p. 683)
    a. True   b. False

23. DDT tends to accumulate in the fatty tissues of organisms. (p. 684)
    a. True   b. False

24. DDT is broken down completely in approximately 12 days after application. (p. 684)
    a. True   b. False

Fill in the Blank

25. It has been estimated that there are approximately_____pounds of DDT currently circulating in the biosphere. (p. 685)

26. _____ _____ authored *Silent Spring*. (p. 686)

27.-29. _____ , _____ , and _____ are three examples of hydrocarbons. (p. 686)

30. _____ is a chlorinated hydrocarbon that interferes with the mobilization of calcium
in the oviduct of birds. (p. 685)

VOCABULARY

These are key words or phrases that you should know. By learning these you will achieve learning goal
number 1. The page where the respective definition occurs is indicated following the word or phrase.

1. smog (p. 678)
2. sulfuric acid (p. 680)
3. engine types (p. 680)
4. radioisotopes (p. 682)

5. mercury poisoning (p. 683)
6. DDT (pp. 684-686)
7. *Silent Spring* (p. 686)
8. chlorinated hydrocarbons (p. 686)

STUDY EXERCISES

Instructions: Write out your answers carefully and completely on a separate paper. Check your
answers by referring to the text page indicated.

1. Describe how smog is formed. (p. 678)
2. Discuss the advantages and disadvantages of nuclear energy. (p. 682)
3. Explain how Eskimos have absorbed more cesium 137 than probably any other group of people on
this planet. (p. 682)
4. What affect does continued accumulation of high levels of mercury have on human tissue? (p. 683)
5. Explain why DDT has so greatly affected the environment of the planet Earth. (pp. 684-686)

SELF-POSTTEST OF LEARNING GOALS

Instructions: After completing the vocabulary and study exercises in written form it is now time to
review. State each definition orally several times. Reread those areas in your text associated with the
study exercises on which you did poorly. Retake the pretest at this time.

ANSWERS

1. a	11. b	21. a
2. c	12. a	22. a
3. b	13. d	23. a
4. c	14. e	24. b
5. a	15. a	25. 1 billion
6. b	16. c	26. Rachel Carson
7. a	17. b	27. chlordane or DDT or
8. a	18. c	28. dieldrin or endrin or
9. b	19. a	29. heptachlor
10. a	20. a	30. DDT

Chapter 44

Prevalence of People

OVERVIEW

For literally thousands and thousands of years the world population of man remained relatively stable. Suddenly, the past few centuries have produced a population increase of almost 3.2 billion. In fact, a 1.5 billion increase has been observed in the last 40 years. At present, because of a dramatic reduction in the mortality rate, the world population is growing at a rate of 180,000 persons per day. If this growth rate continues, there will be approximately 8 billion people on this planet in 30 to 40 years.

It is indeed apparent that the 180,000 persons per day increase in population cannot continue. Thus we will observe a reduction in this growth rate through either wholesale famine, depleted resources, or a controlled birth rate through contraceptive management. The problems of a growing population on this planet are discussed in this chapter.

LEARNING GOALS

After successfully completing this chapter you should, orally or in writing, be able to do the following.

1. Use appropriately the vocabulary associated with this chapter when discussing its concepts.
2. Describe the trend in population growth on this planet since the beginning of the Christian era.
3. State the present daily rate of population growth planet-wide, and relate in which countries the growth is highest.
4. Cite the projected world population by the year 2000, if the present growth trend continues.
5. Relate where approximately two-thirds of the world's people live.
6. Compare the projected increase over the next 30 years between modernized nations and the underdeveloped nations.
7. Identify the two massive population explosions that have been observed on this planet in the last 2000 years.
8. Name the reasons for the reduction in human mortality.
9. Cite the increase in total United States population by the year 2000 if the continued growth rate is 0.8 percent.
10. Explain the demographic transition as it relates to population stabilization.
11. Describe the effect of the green revolution on the control of malnutrition in the world.
12. Discuss the relationship between the pattern of a demographic transition and a contraceptive revolution.
13. State the percent of the earth's population living in the United States and the percent of the world's resources used by these persons.

SELF-PRETEST OF LEARNING GOALS

Before proceeding further in the study of this chapter, attempt to answer the following questions without referring to other information. Upon completion of the test, compare your responses with the answer key at the end of the *Study Guide* chapter. Then correct the wrong responses by referring to the text (page numbers are indicated following each question).

Multiple Choice

1. The annual net gain in population on this planet is approximately (p. 693)
   a. 600 thousand.
   b. 10 million.
   c. 70 million.
   d. 1 billion.
   e. 20 million.

2. The world population at the birth of the Christian era was (p. 693)
   a. 1 billion.
   b. 2 billion.
   c. 3 billion.
   d. 250 million.
   e. 500 million.

3. The present world population is (p. 693)
   a. 1 billion.
   b. 2 billion.
   c. 3 billion.
   d. 4 billion.
   e. 250 million.

4. Which of the following countries has the highest growth rate? (p. 694)
   a. United States
   b. Australia
   c. Germany
   d. Pakistan
   e. Belgium

5. If present fertility and mortality trends persist, how many billion persons will be contending for a place on earth by the year 2000? (p. 694)
   a. 3
   b. 5
   c. 6
   d. 7
   e. 25

6. Acceleration in growth has been rapid. What percentage of the population now living was born since 1945? (p. 693)
   a. 20%
   b. 50%
   c. 80%
   d. 30%
   e. 95%

7. Today, approximately two-thirds of the world's people inhabit (p. 694)
   a. Asia, Europe, and Latin America
   b. Asia, Europe, and Africa
   c. Asia, Africa, and Latin America
   d. Europe, Africa, and Latin America
   e. Asia, Europe, and Australia

8. Projections indicate that by the year 2000 the ratio of persons living in the less developed countries to those living in the affluent countries will be (p. 694)
   a. 2:1.
   b. 8:1.
   c. 3:1.
   d. 10:1.
   e. 20:1.

True—False

9. The two great population explosions were witnessed during the 15th century and after World War II. (pp. 695, 696)
   a. True
   b. False

10. The areas that are today classed as "developed" are Western Europe and Northern America. (p. 696)
    a. True
    b. False

11. The conquest of infectious diseases and the improvement in public health measures during the industrial revolution reduced death rates drastically without having an immediate effect on the birth rate. (p. 697)
   a. True   b. False

12. A rise in the social, economic, and educational levels of people in a society tends to foster a slightly higher birth rate. (p. 696)
   a. True   b. False

13. Annual death rates in the United States are approximately 60 per 1000. (p. 696)
   a. True   b. False

14. Because of new and better public health techniques developed by Western medicine, the death rate has declined in the less developed nations. (p. 696)
   a. True   b. False

15. Many countries in Latin America are growing at a rate that will double the population in 20 to 25 years. (p. 697)
   a. True   b. False

Fill in the Blank

16. The change from very high birth and death rates to a more efficient and humane reproductive pattern of low birth and death rates has been termed the_____. (p. 697)

17. The age range of the female high-fertility group is_____. (pp. 693, 694)

18. The United States has_____ percent of the earth's population. (p. 700)

19. The United States uses about _____ percent of the world's annual production of fossil fuels. (p. 700)

True—False

20. A demographic transition can be broken by a contraceptive revolution. (p. 699)
   a. True   b. False

21. The green revolution has been a fantastic success. (p. 699)
   a. True   b. False

22. The rising aspirations of the poor peoples of the world cannot conceivably be met unless the affluent nations shift their priorities and commit their wealth and power to the survival of mankind. (p. 700)
   a. True   b. False

VOCABULARY

These are key words or phrases that you should know. By learning these you will achieve learning goal number 1. The page where the respective definition occurs is indicated following the word or phrase.

   1. less developed world areas (p. 694)
   2. high fertility age group (pp. 693, 694)
   3. economically advanced world areas (pp. 694)
   4. demographic transition (p. 697)
   5. green revolution (p. 699)
   6. contraceptive revolution (p. 699)

STUDY EXERCISES

Instructions: Write out your answers carefully and completely on a separate paper. Check your answers by referring to the text page indicated.

1. Explain how world population has changed since the time of Christ. (p. 693)
2. Describe the reasons for the decreased death rate planet-wide. (pp. 696, 697)
3. Discuss the steps in a demographic transition. (pp. 696, 697)
4. Explain the green revolution. (p. 699)
5. Describe what the affluent nations must do to establish world-wide nutritional balance. (p. 700)

PROBE

1. Present arguments for and against the continued foreign aid given by the United States to the less-developed countries of the world.

SELF-POSTTEST OF LEARNING GOALS

Instructions: After completing the vocabulary and study exercises in written form it is now time to review. State each definition orally several times. Reread those areas in your text associated with the study exercises on which you did poorly. Retake the pretest at this time.

ANSWERS

1. c
2. d
3. d
4. d
5. d
6. b
7. c
8. c
9. b
10. a
11. a

12. b
13. b
14. a
15. a
16. demographic transition
17. 20-29
18. 6
19. 33
20. a
21. b
22. a

Chapter 45

Biological Rhythms and Clocks

OVERVIEW

Daily rhythms, unknown to most, are an integral part of the normal physiological activity of many plants and animals. Some animals are most active during the daylight hours, while others are most active at night. Many environmental changes are thought to trigger rhythmic changes. This chapter presents materials that will enable you to observe the present varied opinions of the mechanisms of control of the biological rhythms and clocks.

LEARNING GOALS

After successfully completing this chapter you should, orally or in writing, be able to do the following.

1. Use appropriately the vocabulary associated with this chapter when discussing its concepts.
2. Describe the relationship between the fiddler crab and solar rhythmicity.
3. Discuss the various daily rhythms observed in man.
4. State the relationship between lunar rhythmicity and the typical activity of the fiddler crab.
5. Describe the relation between lunar rhythms and sexual reproduction of marine organisms.
6. Compare the views of the endogenous-clock and exogenous-clock hypotheses concerning mechanisms of control.
7. State the medical significance of selected circadian variations.

SELF-PRETEST OF LEARNING GOALS

Before proceeding further in the study of this chapter, attempt to answer the following questions without referring to other information. Upon completion of the test, compare your responses with the answer key at the end of the *Study Guide* chapter. Then correct the wrong responses by referring to the text (page numbers are indicated following each question).

True—False

1. Each day a human's body temperature rises and falls approximately 2°F. (p. 705)
   a. True
   b. False

2. The fiddler crab exhibits a prominent cycle of color changes based on solar rhythmicity. (p. 707)
   a. True
   b. False

3. The crab has the ability to maintain its rhythmic color changes even in the absence of its natural environment. (p. 707)
   a. True
   b. False

4. In man, pulse rate, glucose levels, and blood pressure exhibit cyclical patterns. (pp. 707, 708)
   a. True
   b. False

5. In man, hormones of the adrenal cortex fall to their lowest levels in the late evening. (p. 708)
   a. True   b. False

6. The moon, through its gravitational force, causes the twice-daily tidal cycles. (p. 709)
   a. True   b. False

7. Fiddler crabs exhibit rhythms of locomotary activity that are timed to the tides. (p. 709)
   a. True   b. False

8. The interval of time of a revolution of the moon on its axis is exactly 24 hours. (p. 709)
   a. True   b. False

9. Crabs do not show a rhythmical change in body color as a result of the lunar cycle. (p. 709)
   a. True   b. False

10. Many marine animals show a marked monthly or bimonthly periodicity in sexual reproduction associated with the phases of the moon. (p. 710)
    a. True   b. False

11. The endogenous-clock hypothesis is concerned with autonomous timers within the organism. (pp. 711, 712)
    a. True   b. False

12. Franz Halberg in 1959 coined the term *circadian* to represent an approximate 24-hour cycle. (p. 711)
    a. True   b. False

13. Persons with Addison's disease exhibit a daily rhythm in the level of the white blood cell, eosinophil. (p. 712)
    a. True   b. False

VOCABULARY

These are key words or phrases that you should know. By learning these you will achieve learning goal number 1. The page where the respective definition occurs is indicated following the word or phrase.

1. biological clock (p. 705)
2. solar rhythmicity (pp. 706, 707)
3. lunar rhythmicity (p. 709)
4. endogenous and exogenous clock hypotheses (pp. 711, 712)
5. circadian rhythm (p. 711)

STUDY EXERCISES

Instructions: Write out your answers carefully and completely on a separate paper. Check your answers by referring to the text page indicated.

1. Describe the relationship between solar rhythmicity and body color in the fiddler crab. (pp. 706, 707)
2. Discuss the daily rhythms observed in man. (pp. 707-709)
3. Describe the effect of lunar rhythms on reproduction in the Palolo worm. (pp. 710, 711)
4. Present arguments for and against the endogenous-clock hypothesis. (pp. 711, 712)

SELF-POSTTEST OF LEARNING GOALS

Instructions: After completing the vocabulary and study exercises in written form it is now time to review. State each definition orally several times. Reread those areas in your text associated with the study exercises on which you did poorly. Retake the pretest at this time.

ANSWERS

1. a
2. a
3. a
4. a
5. a
6. a
7. a

8. b
9. b
10. a
11. a
12. a
13. b

Chapter 46

Neural and Motor Bases of Behavior

OVERVIEW

The ability of an organism to survive depends to a great extent on its ability to adapt to conditions that exist in the environment. The adaptive behavior of an organism is partially genetic (instinct) and partially the ability to utilize specific DNA and RNA molecules (learning). To what degree environment effects the inherited character has been debated quite extensively by biologists and psychologists in the last few years. The views that have led scientists to their respective opinions will be presented in this chapter. Concepts concerning the anatomy and physiology of the nervous system (neurobiology) will be correlated to learning and memory.

LEARNING GOALS

After successfully completing this chapter you should, orally or in writing, be able to do the following.

1. Use appropriately the vocabulary associated with this chapter when discussing its concepts.
2. Describe the structure of the neuron.
3. Explain how a nerve impulse is generated and transmitted.
4. State the three functional classes of neurons.
5. Cite what percent of interneurons are found in human nerve cells.
6. Discuss the reflex arc.
7. Describe the mechanism of a typical nerve impulse.
8. Explain the structure and function of the synapse.
9. Describe the neuromuscular junction.
10. State the function of actin and myosin.
11. Discuss the sliding-filament theory of muscle contraction.
12. Compare and contrast the central and autonomic nervous systems.
13. Compare and contrast preganglionic and postaganglionic fibers.
14. Describe the relationship between the nervous and endocrine systems.
15. Cite the relationship between the hypothalamus and the pituitary gland.
16. State the anatomical relationship between the adrenal medulla and the nervous system.
17. Name the three main divisions of the human brain and describe the function of each division.
18. Explain the function of the reticular formation.
19. Describe the behavior of a "split-brain" animal.
20. Discuss present theories of memory.

SELF-PRETEST OF LEARNING GOALS

Before proceeding further in the study of this chapter, attempt to answer the following questions without referring to other information. Upon completion of the test, compare your responses with the answer key at the end of the *Study Guide* chapter. Then correct the wrong responses by referring to the text (page numbers are indicated following each question).

Multiple Choice

1. Which of the following terms signifies that the potential for the behavioral trait is inherited? (p. 717)
   - a. Polygenial
   - b. Innate
   - c. Filitripium
   - d. Psychogenic
   - e. None of these

2. Another term for nerve cell is (p. 717)
   - a. cystoic.
   - b. somatic.
   - c. Ranier's packet.
   - d. neuron.
   - e. none of these.

3. Which of the following is not a part of the nerve cell? (p. 718)
   - a. Nerve fiber
   - b. Axon
   - c. Dendrite
   - d. Node of Ranvier
   - e. Schwann cell
   - f. Kupffer cell

4. Which of the following is not a member of the functional classes of neurons? (p. 718)
   - a. Afferent
   - b. Efferent
   - c. Inter
   - d. Distal
   - e. All of these are members

5. Which of the following conveys nerve impulses away from the nerve cell body? (p. 718)
   - a. Axon
   - b. Dendrite
   - c. Node of Ranvier
   - d. Schwann cells
   - e. None of these

6. Axons are typically covered with a fatty insulating material known as (p. 718)
   - a. cholesterol.
   - b. myelin.
   - c. renin.
   - d. pepsin.
   - e. ergosterol.
   - f. sagitonin.

7. Afferent neurons are also termed (p. 718)
   - a. sensory.
   - b. motor.
   - c. digital.
   - d. convex.
   - e. none of these.

8. Which type of nerve cell is contained wholly within the central nervous system? (p. 718)
   - a. Axon
   - b. Sensory
   - c. Motor
   - d. Interneuron
   - e. None of these

9. In which of the following tissues would the amount of interneurons be the greatest? (p. 718)
   - a. Brain
   - b. Lung
   - c. Liver
   - d. Heart
   - e. Kidney

True—False

10. The number of interneurons in the pathway between afferent and efferent neurons varies according to the complexity of the behavioral action. (p. 719)
    - a. True
    - b. False

11. The chain of neurons leading from the skin receptor to the spinal cord constitutes a reflex arc. (p. 719)
    a. True   b. False

12. If, for example, you were to touch a sharp or hot object and withdraw your hand, the withdrawal of the hand occurs before the sensation of pain is experienced. (p. 719)
    a. True   b. False

13. In a resting state the inside and outside of the nerve membrane is negative. (pp. 720, 721)
    a. True   b. False

14. When a nerve transmission occurs, the membrane is in an active state that will last for approximately 6.25 seconds per stimuli. (p. 722)
    a. True   b. False

15. In all nerve impulses, depolarization occurs immediately following an action potential. (p. 722)
    a. True   b. False

16. It has been demonstrated that the action potential is the result of changes in the permeability of the axon membrane to sodium and potassium ions. (p. 722)
    a. True   b. False

17. The complete restoration of the resting membrane potential involves an outward movement of sodium ions. (p. 722)
    a. True   b. False

Fill in the Blank

18. The axon terminal portion of the synapse releases a chemical substance called a _____. (p. 722)

19. The first chemical substance (mentioned in previous question) to be identified was _____. (p. 723)

20. Only one type of specialized cell in the human body is as capable as the nerve cell in generating an action potential across the cell membrane. This is the _____ cell. (p. 724)

21. The point of contact of the axon's terminal end and the muscle membrane is known as the _____ junction. (p. 724)

22. From a chemical point of view, the contractile components of muscle are two proteins, _____ and _____. (p. 725)

23. A single muscle fiber consists of many _____. (p. 725)

24. In the 1930s, the Hungarian biochemist _____ prepared artificial fibers from precipitated actomyosin and caused contraction by adding ATP. (p. 726)

25. The sliding filament theory of muscle contraction was suggested by _____. (p. 726)

26. Myofibrils are composed of alternating thick and thin subunits known as _____. (p. 725)

True–False

27. Eccles determined that all chemical transmitters are excitatory. (p. 723)
    a. True   b. False

170

28. The cell bodies of afferent neurons are aggregated in small nodules called *ganglia*. (p. 726)
   a. True   b. False

29. The autonomic nervous system is concerned only with the peripheral nerves. (p. 727)
   a. True   b. False

30. Each internal organ under automatic control (such as the heart) receives nerve fibers from each division of the autonomic nervous system. (p. 727)
   a. True   b. False

31. The nerves of the parasympathetic portion of the autonomic nervous system originate from the brain and sacral portion of the spinal cord. (p. 727)
   a. True   b. False

32. Nerve fibers of the sympathetic portion accelerate the heart beat, while fibers from the parasympathetic area slow down the heart rate. (pp. 727, 728)
   a. True   b. False

33. The preganglionic fibers of the parasympathetic division are generally longer than the fibers of the sympathetic division. (pp. 728, 729)
   a. True   b. False

34. Acetylcholine is released by the axons of postganglionic, parasympathetic fibers. (p. 729)
   a. True   b. False

35. Epinephrine is produced by the pancreas. (p. 729)
   a. True   b. False

36. Hormones are transported throughout the body in the blood. (p. 729)
   a. True   b. False

Multiple Choice

37. Which of the following produces releasing factors? (p. 729)
   a. Thyroid   d. Thalamus
   b. Pancreas   e. Adrenal
   c. Hypothalamus   f. All of these

38. Which of the following are directly controlled by the secretions from the anterior pituitary? (p. 729)
   a. Thyroid   d. Testes
   b. Adrenal cortex   e. All of these
   c. Ovaries   f. None of these

39. Which of the following is produced by the adrenal medulla? (p. 729)
   a. Thyroxine   d. Testosterone
   b. Epinephrine   e. None of these
   c. Cortisone

40. Which endocrine gland is regarded as an "overgrown" sympathetic ganglion? (p. 729)
   a. Thyroid   d. Liver
   b. Ovary   e. None of these
   c. Pancreas

Matching

41. Cerebrum (p. 731)
42. Cerebellum (p. 731)
43. Reticular formation (p. 731)
44. Thalamus (p. 732)
45. Hypothalamus (p. 732)

a. controls pituitary
b. relay center
c. coordination
d. taste
e. coughing
f. none of these

True—False

46. The cerebral cortex is divided into lobes. (p. 731)
  a. True
  b. False

47. An animal with the cerebral hemispheres divided behaves as if it had two separate brains. (p. 732)
  a. True
  b. False

48. Memory, according to Holger Hyden, is the accumulation of RNA molecules. (pp. 732, 733)
  a. True
  b. False

49. Brain extracts from selected animals have been injected into other animals with one result being the transfer of memory. (p. 733)
  a. True
  b. False

50. At present, there is no general agreement among investigators concerning the actual mechanism of learning or memory. (p. 733)
  a. True
  b. False

VOCABULARY

These are key words or phrases that you should know. By learning these you will achieve learning goal number 1. The page where the respective definition occurs is indicated following the word or phrase.

1. innate (p. 717)
2. neuron (p. 717)
3. nerve fiber (p. 717)
4. nerve impulse (pp. 717, 718)
5. synapse (p. 718)
6. dendrite (p. 718)
7. axon (p. 718)
8. myelin (p. 718)
9. Schwann cell (p. 718)
10. nodes of Ranvier (p. 718)
11. classes of neurons (p. 718)
12. reflex arc (p. 719)
13. resting potential (p. 720)
14. polarized (p. 720)
15. depolarization (p. 720)
16. action potential (p. 722)
17. sodium pump (p. 722)
18. transmitter (p. 722)
19. synaptic knob (p. 723)
20. synaptic vesicle (p. 723)

21. acetylcholine (p. 723)
22. neuromuscular junction (p. 724)
23. actin and myosin (p. 725)
24. myofibril (p. 725)
25. filament (p. 725)
26. sliding-filament theory (p. 726)
27. peripheral nerves (p. 726)
28. ganglia (p. 726)
29. autonomic nervous system (p. 727)
30. preganglionic fiber (pp. 728, 729)
31. postganglionic fiber (pp. 728, 729)
32. epinephrine (p. 729)
33. releasing factor (p. 729)
34. hypothalamus (p. 732)
35. brain (pp. 729-732)
36. cerebrum (pp. 731, 732)
37. cerebellum (p. 731)
38. reticular formation (pp. 730, 731)
39. thalamus (p. 732)
40. split-brain (p. 732)

STUDY EXERCISES

Instructions: Write out your answers carefully and completely on separate paper. Check your answers by referring to the text page indicated.

1. Describe a neuron. (pp. 717, 718)
2. Discuss the nature of a nerve impulse. (p. 720)
3. Explain how electrical information is transmitted from one neuron to another and from a nerve to a muscle cell. (pp. 721-726)
4. How does the autonomic nervous system differ from the peripheral nervous system? (pp. 726-729)
5. Directly or indirectly, how does the hypothalamus control the adrenal cortex? (p. 729)

SELF-POSTTEST OF LEARNING GOALS

Instructions: After completing the vocabulary and study exercises in written form it is now time to review. State each definition orally several times. Reread those areas in your text associated with the study exercises on which you did poorly. Retake the pretest at this time.

ANSWERS

1. b	26. filaments
2. d	27. b
3. f	28. a
4. d	29. b
5. a	30. a
6. b	31. a
7. a	32. a
8. d	33. a
9. a	34. a
10. a	35. b
11. b	36. a
12. a	37. c
13. b	38. e
14. b	39. b
15. a	40. e
16. a	41. d
17. a	42. c
18. transmitter	43. f
19. acetylcholine	44. b
20. muscle	45. a
21. neuromuscular	46. a
22. actin and myosin	47. a
23. myofibrils	48. a
24. Szent-Gyorgi	49. a
25. Huxley	50. a

Chapter 47

Ethology: The Comparative Study of Behavior

OVERVIEW

Man has for centuries attempted to study the behavior of higher animals. Most attempts were futile because true behavior cannot be observed when an organism is in captivity. Because of this, the field of ethology was born. Ethology is the study of animal's habitual behavior in its natural environment. Behavior from the ethologist's point of view will be presented in this chapter, with emphasis placed on factors that influence behavior.

LEARNING GOALS

After successfully completing this chapter you should, orally or in writing, be able to do the following.

1. Describe ethology.
2. Use appropriately the vocabulary associated with this chapter when discussing its concepts.
3. Explain fixed patterns of behavior.
4. Describe the role of a sign stimulus in the triggering of a given behavioral act.
5. Discuss the relationship between inhibition removal and the innate releasing mechanism (IRM).
6. Explain a reaction chain that occurs between two animals.
7. State what imprinting is and why it is a distinctive form of learning.
8. Cite the motivation for appeasement behavior.
9. Compare and contrast redirected and displacement behavioral activities.
10. Relate the role of genetics in behavior.
11. Explain why aggression occurs in all animals.

SELF-PRETEST OF LEARNING GOALS

Before proceeding further in the study of this chapter, attempt to answer the following questions without referring to other information. Upon completion of the test, compare your responses with the answer key at the end of the *Study Guide* chapter. Then correct the wrong responses by referring to the text (page numbers are indicated following each question).

Fill in the Blank

1. _____ is the comparative study of the behavioral characteristics of species. (p. 737)

2. If a behavioral act is inherited it is said to be _____ . (p. 737)

3. Konrad Lorenz defines innate behavioral acts as _____ patterns. (p. 737)

4. The general restlessness of an animal has been called _____ behavior. (p. 739)

5. A given behavioral act is triggered by a _____ stimulus. (p. 739)

6. Lorenz and Tinbergen postulated that inhibitions are removed by an _____ _____ mechanism. (p. 740)

174

True—False

7. If a frog flicks his tongue at a moving organism or object, this represents a consummatory act. (p. 739)
   a. True   b. False

8. Each innate releasing mechanism responds to a releaser. (p. 740)
   a. True   b. False

9. If an organism learns to be selective in his prey, based on past experience, a negative conditioning, or habituation, has occurred. (p. 741)
   a. True   b. False

10. Releasers have one form and affect behavioral mechanisms in a like manner. (p. 741)
    a. True   b. False

11. In many courtship rituals, each animal's actions serve as a releaser for the other animal's subsequent reponse. (p. 743)
    a. True   b. False

12. The capacity for recognizing appropriate sign stimuli is a learned phenomenon. (p. 745)
    a. True   b. False

13. Imprinting is the result of behavioral modification. (p. 745)
    a. True   b. False

14. The appeasement behavior of an animal reduces the incidence of aggression. (p. 746)
    a. True   b. False

15. Redirected activity is a type of behavioral conflict. (p. 748)
    a. True   b. False

16. Displacement activity occurs when two motivations are in conflict with each other. (p. 748)
    a. True   b. False

17. Behavioral patterns are as much a product of the evolutionary process as are adaptive morphological structures. (p. 748)
    a. True   b. False

18. Aggression in all animals is part of the organism's adaptive response to its environment. (p. 749)
    a. True   b. False

VOCABULARY

These are key words or phrases that you should know. By learning these you will achieve learning goal number 2. The page where the respective definition occurs is indicated following the word or phrase.

1. ethology (p. 737)
2. innate (p. 737)
3. fixed patterns (p. 737)
4. appetitive behavior (p. 739)
5. motivational drive (p. 739)
6. consummatory act (p. 739)
7. innate releasing mechanism (p. 740)

8. releaser (p. 740)
9. habituation (p. 741)
10. imprinting (p. 745)
11. appeasement (p. 746)
12. redirected activity (p. 748)
13. displacement activity (p. 748)

STUDY EXERCISES

Instructions: Write out your answers carefully and completely on separate paper. Check your answers by referring to the text page indicated.

1. Compare and contrast redirected and displacement behavioral activities. (p. 748)
2. Describe reasons for the aggressive behavior evident in all animals, including man. (pp. 749-750)

SELF-POSTTEST OF LEARNING GOALS

Instructions: After completing the vocabulary and study exercises in written form it is now time to review. State each definition orally several times. Reread those areas in your test associated with the study exercises on which you did poorly. Retake the pretest at this time.

ANSWERS

1. Ethology	10. b
2. innate	11. a
3. fixed	12. b
4. appetitive	13. a
5. sign	14. a
6. innate releasing	15. b
7. a	16. a
8. a	17. a
9. a	18. a

Chapter 48

Social Behavior

OVERVIEW

The interactions of animals in a society is not limited to just man. Most birds and mammals exhibit a striking social order. Grouping of animals tends to enhance social orders and it also provides protection from predators. In order for large schools, flocks, or herds to exist, a social order and specific cooperative behavior must be present. Materials will be presented which detail how social behavior develops and how it enhances the ability of animal groups to survive.

LEARNING GOALS

After successfully completing this chapter you should be able, orally or in writing, to do the following.

1. Use appropriately the vocabulary associated with this chapter when discussing its concepts.
2. Describe the establishment of a dominance hierarchy.
3. Discuss the relationship between position in the dominance hierarchy and reproductive success.
4. Explain how a matriarchal society functions.
5. Describe a typical day in the life of a baboon, utilizing the role of dominance and the relationship between all members of the troop.
6. Present man's association with social control and dominance behavior.
7. Cite the role of territoriality in organizing societies.
8. Describe what may have caused territorial behavior in man.
9. Name examples of mammals where the male plays an important role in the social interactions of mother and child.
10. Compare the advancement in neural growth of newly born primates.
11. Describe the findings from the studies by Harlow concerning the utilization of pseudomothers by baby rhesus monkeys.
12. Discuss the factors that contributed to the establishment of the human family.

SELF-PRETEST OF LEARNING GOALS

Before proceeding further in the study of this chapter, attempt to answer the following questions without referring to other information. Upon completion of the test, compare your responses with the answer key at the end of the *Study Guide* chapter. Then correct the wrong responses by referring to the text (page numbers are indicated following each question).

True—False

1. The peck order observed in chickens is an example of dominance hierarchy. (p. 755)
   a. True   b. False

2. In social groups characterized by dominance hierarchies, it can be shown that the high-ranking animals have the greatest reproductive success. (p. 755)
   a. True   b. False

3. In dominance hierarchies the dominant member has priority of access to food. (p. 755)
   a. True   b. False

4. Dominance hierarchies do not occur in the primate. (p. 758)
   a. True   b. False

5. Young female baboons remain in close and dependent contact with their mother for many years. (p. 757)
   a. True   b. False

6. In a matriarchal society the female, following rut, assumes the primary responsibility of maintaining the herd. (p. 756)
   a. True   b. False

7. The African baboon generally remains in the forest area during the day. (p. 756)
   a. True   b. False

8. The baboon normally moves in troops of 30 to 50 individuals. (p. 756)
   a. True   b. False

Fill in the Blank

9. _____ is a type of organization that is closely connected with dominance in the control of aggression in the animal societies. (p. 758)

10. _____ and _____ are examples of animals among which the male plays an important role in the social interactions of mother and child. (p. 761)

11. Approximately _____ years ago man began to raise crops and domesticate herds. (p. 761)

Matching

12. Morris (p. 761)   a. author of *The Territorial Imperative*
13. Ardrey (p. 760)   b. studied family unit of chimpanzees
14. van Lawick (p. 761)   c. studied pseudomothers in monkeys
15. Harlow (p. 763)   d. proposed territoriality for man since 8000 B.C.
16. Barnes (p. 761)   e. author of *Naked Ape*

VOCABULARY

These are key words or phrases that you should know. By learning these you will achieve learning goal number 1. The page where the respective definition occurs is indicated following the word or phrase.

1. dominance hierarchy (p. 755)   5. lek (p. 759)
2. peck order (p. 755)   6. *Naked Ape* (p. 761)
3. rut (p. 756)   7. matriarchal society (p. 756)
4. territoriality (p. 758)   8. pseudomother (pp. 763-764)

STUDY EXERCISES

Instructions: Write out your answers carefully and completely on separate paper. Check your answers by referring to the text page indicated.

1. Describe how a peck order is established among a group of chickens. (p. 755)
2. Explain how dominance hierarchy expresses itself in a herd of red deer. (p. 756)
3. Discuss the general activities of a troop of baboons when confronted with danger while feeding on the savanna. (pp. 756-575)
4. Describe territoriality as it relates to lek formation. (pp. 759-760)
5. Does territoriality exist in higher primates? Compare it between man and the chimpanzee. (pp. 758, 760-761)
6. Relate the presence of a pseudomother to the development of social behavioral patterns in rhesus monkeys. (pp. 763-764)

SELF-POSTTEST OF LEARNING GOALS

Instructions: After completing the vocabulary in written form it is now time to review. State each definition orally several times. Reread those areas in your text associated with the study exercises on which you did poorly. Retake the pretest at this time.

ANSWERS

1. a
2. a
3. a
4. b
5. a
6. a
7. b
8. a

9. Territoriality
10. Wolves and humans
11. 10,000
12. e
13. a
14. b
15. c
16. d

Chapter 49

Man's Cultural Adaptation

OVERVIEW

Man for thousands of years was a hunter traveling from area to area in search of food. Approximately 10,000 years ago man learned how to grow crops and domesticate animals. This advance allowed him to change his entire lifestyle simply because for the first time he was, in a small way, controlling nature instead of being at its mercy. Man realized the advantages of living in communities and civilizations began to flourish. From this meager beginning at about 8000 B.C. man has advanced to his present status on the planet Earth. This chapter presents materials concerning cultural evolution and what influence these changes have had on the biology of man and his lifestyle.

LEARNING GOALS

After successfully completing this chapter you should, orally or in writing, be able to do the following.

1. Use appropriately the vocabulary associated with this chapter when discussing its concepts.
2. Describe the difference between biological and cultural evolution.
3. Relate how the art of dentistry is a cultural adaptation.
4. Discuss what causes the acceptance of a given cultural innovation.
5. State the statistical association between cigarette smoking and lung cancer.
6. Describe factors that appear to influence attitudes toward cigarette smoking.
7. Discuss how food additives produce deleterious effects in the human population.
8. Cite the main problem in global malnutrition.
9. Explain kwashiorkor and marasmus.
10. Describe why many of the less developed nations have severe malnutrition.
11. State what percentage of the total United States population is over 65 years of age and what percentage of the aged suffer from one or more chronic diseases.
12. Discuss the disadvantages of being elderly in the United States.

SELF-PRETEST OF LEARNING GOALS

Before proceeding further in the study of this chapter, attempt to answer the following questions without referring to other information. Upon completion of the test, compare your responses with the answer key at the end of the *Study Guide* chapter. Then correct the wrong responses by referring to the text (page numbers are indicated following each question).

True—False

1. Cultural and biological evolution occurs at essentially the same rate. (p. 769)
   a. True   b. False

2. Cultural evolution has no effect on man's lifestyle. (p. 769)
   a. True   b. False

3. A given cultural change can be passed on to large groups of unrelated individuals. (p. 769)
   a. True   b. False

4. Biological evolution depends on accidental mutational changes in the DNA molecule. (p. 769)
   a. True   b. False

5. The magnitude of human pregnancy wasteage is approximately 50 percent. (p. 770)
   a. True   b. False

6. Cultural evolution does supersedes biological evolution. (p. 770)
   a. True   b. False

7. Whereas other species must await the appropriate alterations in their genetic composition to adapt to environmental changes, man responds to changes by modifying his culture. (p. 770)
   a. True   b. False

8. The art of dentistry is a cultural adaptation. (p. 771)
   a. True   b. False

9. People are generally united on medical measures that genuinely safeguard health. (p. 771)
   a. True   b. False

10. Communicable diseases have, by and large, been conquered. (p. 771)
    a. True   b. False

11. The statistical association between cigarette smoking and lung cancer strongly indicates a cause-and-effect relation. (p. 772)
    a. True   b. False

12. The primary impetus for smoking is thought to derive from underlying needs and longings within the person. (p. 772)
    a. True   b. False

13. Cyclamates produced bladder cancer in rats. (p. 774)
    a. True   b. False

14. The key problem of nutrition on this planet is a shortage of high-carbohydrate foods. (p. 774)
    a. True   b. False

15. Protein insufficiency afflicts approximately 25 percent of the world's children. (p. 774)
    a. True   b. False

16. Kwashiorkor is a condition of acute protein starvation that appears shortly after weaning, when the child is fed predominantly cereal grains. (p. 774)
    a. True   b. False

17. Marasmus occurs when a child's diet is deficient in both calories and protein. (p. 775)
    a. True   b. False

18. All essential amino acids are typically furnished by animal products. (p. 775)
    a. True   b. False

19. The proportion of citizens over 65 years of age in the United States is about 8 percent of the total population. (p. 776)
    a. True   b. False

20. Approximately 86 percent of the aged suffer from one or more chronic diseases. (p. 776)
    a. True   b. False

21. The taking of life of an infant is termed infanticide. (p. 776)
   a. True   b. False

22. Euthanasia is the deliberate taking of a person's life in the event of an incurable, painful, or terminal illness. (p. 777)
   a. True   b. False

VOCABULARY

These are key words that you should know. By learning these you will achieve learning goal number 1. The page where the respective definition occurs is indicated following the word or phrase.

1. cultural evolution (p. 769)   4. marasmus (p. 775)
2. cyclamate (p. 774)   5. infanticide (p. 776)
3. kwashiorkor (p. 774)   6. euthanasia (p. 777)

STUDY EXERCISES

Instructions: Write out your answers carefully and completely on separate paper. Check your answer by referring to the text page indicated.

1. Compare and contrast biological and cultural evolution. (p. 769)
2. What, at present, is the greatest world-wide nutritional problem? (pp. 774-776)

PROBE

1. Why do you think cirgarette smoking continues at a high level considering the incidence of lung cancer?
2. Do you think there is a feasible solution to the world protein problem? Explain.
3. What are your personal feelings concerning infanticide and euthanasia?

SELF-POSTTEST OF LEARNING GOALS

Instructions: After completing the vocabulary and study exercises in written form it is now time to review. State each definition orally several times. Reread those areas in your text associated with the study exercises on which you did poorly. Retake the pretest at this time.

ANSWERS

1. b	12. a
2. b	13. a
3. a	14. b
4. a	15. b
5. a	16. a
6. b	17. a
7. a	18. a
8. a	19. b
9. a	20. a
10. b	21. a
11. a	22. a